THE CHILDREN'S WAR

The Children's War

*Evacuees on a north
Pembrokeshire Farm*

Ken Foskett

ISBN: 1-84524-062-6
13 ISBN: 978-1-84524-062-2

Cover design: Dylan Williams

Published by
Llygad Gwalch, Ysgubor Plas, Llwyndyrys, Pwllheli,
Gwynedd, Wales LL53 6NG.
☎ 01758 750432   ▤ 01758 750438
✆ gai@llygadgwalch.com

CONTENTS

INTRODUCTION

It was the 18th June, 1940 when Churchill gave his most rousing speech.

'We will fight them on the beaches,' he proclaimed, as England stood alone and waited for the German army to land. Defences were quickly erected and minefields laid, but most of the British army's equipment had been left behind on the beaches of Dunkirk. It was deemed necessary to evacuate a ten mile strip along the coastline of Kent and Sussex; children were given priority.

Eight hundred and seventy four years had passed since the last invasion of England, when William the Conqueror came ashore with his army in 1066. He defeated King Harold in the ensuing battle a few miles inland on a hill at Senlac. To commemorate his victory, William built an abbey on that spot and the place became known as Battle. It was from here, in the dawn on the 21st June, 1940, that a family left their home in Harold Terrace and walked down the hill to the station.

With head down, a twelve year old girl led the way through the half light, followed by her eight year old brother who was still half asleep. They each carried a small suitcase and had a gas mask in its cardboard box strung over one shoulder. With worried looks on their faces the parents followed in silence. Although still early, the day was quite mild and, with the exception of the father, they all wore light clothing. He wore the uniform of an army officer complete with highly polished Sam Browne and carried a swagger stick. Deep in their own thoughts, they didn't notice the stench as they walked past the tannery before crossing the railway bridge then, turning right, down the short walk to the station. The father checked his watch as the train was already waiting at the platform where small groups were standing as if reluctant to board.

A group of officials stood at the entrance and check-lists were consulted and details exchanged. Identity cards, ration books, gas masks and cases were all thoroughly examined before each child had a label pinned on. This gave the name and other relevant information, but it did not state a destination.

A short walk along the platform soon led to the correct carriage and the allocated compartment which was already nearly full of children. In charge was a worried looking teacher who confirmed the information on the labels with her check-list.

There was nothing left to do now, so, trying to hold back their tears, the two children said their good-byes and climbed aboard to become two more statistics out of three million children evacuated because of the war.

This is their story.

Chapter 1

THE JOURNEY

Although I had never been separated from my parents before I was not too upset when the train pulled out of the station. Our parents had assured us that we would be safe and well cared for, and that it would only be for a short time. The teacher also tried to calm everyone down by saying we were not travelling very far and I was lucky to have an older sister to lean on. Besides, I loved to ride in a train. We always went by train for our summer holidays. I always used to insist on walking up front to inspect the engine. I would note its number and name, displayed with pride in polished brass, before acknowledging the crew; it worried me a little that I had forgotten to do so on this journey. It also upset me not to have secured a window seat (when travelling with my family I was always given the seat next to the window) and I determined to alter that situation somehow before long.

Rene appeared to be the senior girl in our compartment and she didn't look very happy. She kept blowing her nose which made her eyes red and watery, or so she said. She was seated opposite me and next to the teacher who was doing most of the talking and trying to cheer her up. We were very close and I hated to see my sister upset but I couldn't think of anything to say or do to make her smile.

At the start of the journey everyone sat very quietly and lost in thought but, as is normal with kids, they became restless as time marched on. The teacher tried to distract them with food and drinks which soon resulted in a steady demand for the toilet. Thank goodness for corridor trains! All this movement in and out of our compartment I used to my advantage, and eventually secured a window seat. This was only a temporary arrangement, however, as I too, eventually had to answer nature's call.

The day warmed up. Sandwiches and cold drinks were produced for lunch. Nobody seemed very hungry and a few of the little children became sick and had accidents before they could reach the toilet. This caused our compartment to smell almost like the toilet which upset everyone as the day grew hotter.

Things quietened down during the afternoon and most of the kids were dozing when we heard what we thought were bombs close by, but our teacher told us not to worry, that it was only our soldiers having gun practice. However, after this incident, the train took some twists and turns away from the cities and, at times, seemed to have turned completely around and to be taking us home.

Rene helped the teacher to amuse the children with games and stories, though by evening everyone became restless. As it cooled down some managed to doze and even the teacher's eyes were closed at times.

Suddenly we all awoke with a start. It had become dark outside and our compartment was only faintly lit by one small globe. The train was making a different noise but the teacher reassured everyone by explaining that we were in a long tunnel. It seemed ages before we came out into the light again and by now everyone was awake and looking out of the window. The scenery had changed dramatically, as if we were in a different country.

Rene came and sat next to me and we looked out to one side where the ocean was almost lapping the railway track, whilst on the opposite side we could see mountains sweeping down to the sea. As the sun set, to be replaced by a full moon, the landscape took on an eerie look. In the moonlight the massive grey rocks looked cold and the deep crevices black and menacing in the shadows. Vegetation was sparse and the few trees were stunted and leaning at a crazy angle, testimony to the velocity of the winter storms. There was no doubt that wherever we were, we were in a harsh country.

The never ending clickerty-clack of the wheels had a hypnotic effect and most of the children slept again, exhausted by the traumatic events of the day. Two or three of the little ones were still sobbing and the teacher did her best to pacify them. One climbed onto Rene's lap and although it must have been uncomfortable for her, she did not protest. I felt envious and wished it was me being cuddled but, of course, being eight years old I was too grown up for that nonsense or so my father had told me. Closing my eyes, I thought about the happy times we had shared as a family and wondered when we would all be back together again.

I awoke in alarm wondering where I was and what was going on. My sister was shaking me and as I came to my senses I realised that the train had stopped and someone had opened the door. We were told to gather up our belongings and stand outside. The first thing that struck us was the cold wind blowing from the sea and, dressed in our light summer clothing, we were soon shivering with cold.

Tables had been set out along the platform on which platters of sandwiches and cakes and cold drinks had been placed. But my attention was drawn to the ladies standing behind the tables. They were conversing amongst themselves in a strange language but when they invited us to help ourselves to the food they spoke in English, albeit with a sing-song accent.

The ladies were all keen to know where we had come from and if we had been bombed. They wanted to know all about our homes and our parents. We were literally bombarded with questions which we soon found disconcerting, especially as we didn't yet know where we were or who the ladies were.

The teacher came to our rescue and answered their questions as best she could while we ate. Then, turning her attention to us, she told us we were in Wales but our journey was still not finished and she pointed to two rather small and dilapidated buses parked close by.

We were more tired and cold than hungry and were relieved to be loaded into the buses out of the wind. At first we went very slowly through the narrow streets, sometimes squeezing between the buildings with only inches to spare. On the outskirts of the town we were confronted by a steep climb up an open headland. As the over-crowded bus climbed the steep rise the motor screamed in protest and the smell of hot oil and petrol filled the interior. There was an ever increasing sheer drop on one side and to make things more interesting we had to negotiate two U turns.

As we climbed higher the view became more spectacular. We could see across the town to another headland at the base of which was the harbour, from where, we were told, the ferries made the crossing to Ireland. This, of course, had ceased because of the war.

On reaching the top of the headland there was only one way to go, down! It seemed that the two buses were having a race as we flew down the hills and leaned alarmingly as we negotiated the sharp bends along the tortuous coast road with the ocean on the one side and the mountains on the other. We flashed through one tiny village, a few lime washed cottages standing out starkly in the brilliant moonlight, before stopping a few miles further on outside the hall of another, larger village. We had arrived, a little shaken but safe.

We had no idea what was going to happen to us and Rene and I kept close together as we left the bus and entered the hall. At the doorway some ladies were seated at a table and they checked our labels and our belongings and entered our particulars on some forms. After a few questions we were told to stand against the wall with the other children.

Looking about us we saw groups of ladies standing around, talking together in Welsh. There were few men, but I did notice a minister wearing a dog collar.

When the last of the evacuees entered the hall the ladies started to circulate and ask questions. Some of these were quite personal which I did not understand, but they upset Rene and made her red in the face. They asked about our health and about our parents. On learning that our father was an army officer, and being assured that I was not a bedwetter, a few started to offer one of us a home. Nobody wanted us both. The problem seemed to be that none of the cottages in the village had two spare bedrooms and it was considered inappropriate for Rene and I to share.

The hall emptied quite quickly as the children were accommodated, and this put Rene under intense pressure as she had promised our mother that under no circumstances would we be separated. Soon we were the only ones left standing against the wall and my sister burst into tears. The day's trauma and being made responsible for me were just too much for her to bear. Of course, this upset me too. Up to this point I had had a big sister watching over me but now she needed someone to look after her and all I could do was cry with her. My father was always telling me that big boys don't cry but right at that moment I did not feel like being a big boy. I felt very small and vulnerable.

A tall, thin parson detached himself from a group of people standing near the door and came towards us. He was wearing a clerical collar under his black suit and I could see little beads of perspiration on his bald head as he learned over to comfort us. In between sobs Rene explained our predicament and added that we desperately wanted to stay on a farm. This rather surprised me as we had never discussed this before but I was happy to go long with whatever my big sister wanted.

Telling us to dry our tears and not to worry and omising that he would help us, he returned to the group ladies by the door. After a lengthy conversation, one of the ladies came over to us. She was short and round and, like nearly all of the other ladies, was dressed in black. Her cheeks were like rosy red apples and a pair of wire framed spectacles perched precariously on the tip of her nose. Her long silver hair was secured on the top of her head in a bun, upon which a small black hat was perched, secured by a multitude of hat pins and giving the overall effect of a pin cushion. Her pale blue eyes had a softness about them but they also twinkled with a spark of humour. We liked her instantly.

After checking that we were keen to live on a farm, she told us we were welcome to stay with her, but warned us it would not be easy. She went on to explain that the farm was three miles from the village which meant a long walk to school, which would be especially hard in the winter. Also, there was only one spare bedroom and we would have to share a double bed. But, winter was a long way off and by this time we would have slept in a haystack. I could see the look of relief spread over Rene's face as we picked up our belongings and followed Mrs Ladd to the door. Our journey still had not finished, we had three more miles to go.

We had our labels checked for the last time and Mrs Ladd spent a few minutes talking to the ladies behind the table before finally stepping outside into the cold night air. We were joined by the minister who led us to a tiny Austin 7 where he helped Rene and me squeeze into the back with our luggage before helping Mrs Ladd into the front seat. This became a problem as Mrs Ladd was wider than the door! Eventually, with much pushing and shoving she was in and the door was shut, but now the little car had a pronounced lean to one side and there appeared to be no room for the driver who was at the front turning the crank handle. The engine soon started and was running smoothly. The little car seemed quite neat and well cared for, even the canvas hood and side curtains all seemed to fit well. The problem which now confronted the driver was how to get in! What with Mrs Ladd being so large, and the minister so tall, it was akin to a praying mantis trying to get into a match box! We need not have worried, however, for our driver obviously had much experience to his credit and we watched as he put on a very talented act that would have been the envy of any contortionist in a circus. With the minister behind the wheel, the little car returned to an almost even keel, but there was now another problem; the gear lever had disappeared! After some cautious exploring it was located under Mrs Ladd and after a protesting crunch from the gear box we were on our way. We passed through the village and immediately started to climb. Bright moonlight shone on the remains of an old castle and on the opposite side white grave stones shone brightly against the dark lawn which surrounded a grey stone church.

Hedgerows grew from behind low walls built from the grey mountain stone. These bordered both sides of the road which was only wide enough for one vehicle. Without warning the road made a sharp ninety degree turn and there, straight ahead of us, was the steepest hill I had ever seen. Rene and I both looked ahead in horror as we realised our driver was going to attempt the impossible. Surely, we thought this over-laden, under powered little car was never going to make it to the top and to roll back down and crash into the rock walls would be suicidal. We hit the bottom of the hill with the gear box screaming in low gear and were only half way up when the engine started to labour.

Our driver's knuckles shone white as he gripped the wheel hard. His lips were moving but no sound was coming out; he must have been praying. Mrs Ladd seemed oblivious of our predicament and still carried on her conversation with the minister, even though he was totally preoccupied. But his prayers must have been answered and our little car just made it to the top of the hill, with a few wisps of steam coming from the radiator cap.

Picking up speed again, we passed, on one side, several cottages silhouetted against the backdrop of the mountain and below us small stone walled fields proclaimed the farmer's constant battle against the mountain. The road levelled out, appearing to run downhill in the distance towards the mouth of the valley. But not for us the easy way! The minister steered the little car off the narrow bitumen road and onto an unsurfaced track. This led us past a small farm before heading across the open face of the mountain. We now had a good view of the peaks which consisted of a pile of huge rocks once thrust from the bowels of the earth by some gigantic force of nature and scattered far and wide. Stunted gorse bushes and bracken competed for the space between the rocks, and a myriad of white blobs were scattered across the landscape. At our approach these turned into black faced sheep who nimbly made their escape.

Below us we caught glimpses of the road leading to the valley and some cottages. We could see neat fields on the slopes of the rolling hills that reached the horizon and below these we could make out the course of a small river

16

as it made its way to the sea. Though tired and apprehensive, Rene and I just couldn't take our eyes away from the beauty that surrounded us and made even more spectacular by the bright moonlight.

We ceased climbing and the track levelled out as it became enclosed between the inevitable stone walls and our view was restricted to glimpses of fields as we passed a gate. The fact that we were now in farming country was confirmed when a pack of dogs burst out of a farmyard gate, barking savagely. They tried to bite the tyres and chased us for quite a distance. Throughout the drive Mrs Ladd had continued her one sided conversation, in Welsh, with the minister whose only contribution was a grunt or nod of the head when Mrs Ladd paused for breath. Occasionally, she would half turn to ask us a question, talking very loudly in a shrill voice in order to be heard above the noise of the engine. We were rather overwhelmed by her, being confined in the limited space of the small car.

Although tired we were wide awake and too tense to sleep. We just sat in silence, staring ahead and anticipating the first glimpse of our new home. We didn't have long to wait before the little car suddenly slowed down as the lane made a sharp turn to the right and we saw, directly in front of us, a typical Welsh farmhouse.

Entering the farmyard through the open gate, the minister pulled up in front of the house and switched off the engine. Our journey was complete. We had arrived.

Chapter 2

THE ARRIVAL

The minister climbed out of the car and ran around to help Mrs Ladd, who, when finally extricated, left the car like a cork leaving a bottle. During this time she had never stopped talking and was now carrying on a shouted conversation with someone coming from the house. Two dogs added to the confusion as they came bounding from the porch barking loudly and ran straight at Rene and me. The smaller dog was a black and white sheep dog who wagged her tail as she sniffed Rene all over, but the other dog was much bigger and looked like a wolf and he growled at me in a most menacing manner. His hair bristled and long white fangs were exposed behind his curled lips. I was frightened but, thankfully, a man's shout sent both dogs immediately back to the porch. The minister took his leave, giving Rene and me a pat on the head assuring us we were in good hands and that we had nothing to worry about. We all stood and watched the little car disappear down the lane in quite a sprightly fashion, glad to be going down hill, no longer overburdened. Picking up our meagre belongings, we followed Mrs Ladd into the house.

On each side of the porch were wooden benches under

which the two dogs now lay. As we passed through, we received a tail wag from one side and a growl from the other, which I found to be rather disconcerting; however neither dog moved. We entered a small passage and directly in front of us rose a wooden staircase on either side of which was a door. The one on our left was open and we were led through it into the large kitchen. I will never forget entering Dolrannog on that first night.

It took a while for my eyes to adjust to the dimness as the full moon gave a far brighter light outside than did the solitary oil lamp that was standing on the table inside. Also, the air outside had been clear and crisp while inside, the atmosphere was stifling. This was caused not only by smoke from the fire and fumes from the lamp, but equally by the strong tobacco the men were smoking in their pipes or hand rolled cigarettes.

The one little window was blacked out letting neither air nor light in or out, and was too small to have made much difference anyway. The room seemed crowded with people of all different ages, shapes and sizes and I noticed one very new baby being rocked in its mother's arms.

The babble of voices ceased as Mrs Ladd led us into the room like performers onto a stage. She introduced us first to Mr Ladd and their grown-up daughter Megan and younger son Benny, then to all the relatives and friends with names we had never heard before and could not pronounce, let alone remember.

Then came the inevitable questions. They wanted to know all about our home and parents, if we had been bombed and if we had been starved by the rationing. The fact that our father was an army Captain again made an impression and they wanted to know what battles he had fought in and whether he had won any medals. As the questions became more probing I could see my sister becoming upset, because, although they asked the questions in English they would then discuss the answers amongst themselves in Welsh. I decided to act dumb but I could not help letting my eyes wander in fascination, for I had never been in a room like this one before.

Above me strong wooden beams spanned the thick stone walls and resting across them varnished boards formed the ceiling and the floor above. Wooden slats had been fixed across some of the beams to form storage racks which contained a conglomeration of tins and boxes. An antique shotgun was noticeable as were dozens of long bars of soap, some red, some white. One object completely baffled me. It looked like a set of bagpipes with a bow from a violin attached. I determined to satisfy my curiosity and ask somebody about it later. Hooks had been fixed to the beams from which hung hams and pieces of bacon which had been cured then smoked.

In the middle of the room stood a large round table covered by a well worn oil cloth whose pattern was too faded to distinguish. In the centre stood the solitary lamp. Around the table, eight people sat on an odd assortment of chairs.

Under the window was an old leatherette couch joined at one end by a similar one which provided seating next to the fire on one side of the ingle-nook. An uncomfortable wooden settle served the same purpose on the other side.

The flickering flames from the fire in the huge black kitchen range gave little light in the ingle-nook where the smoke drifted up to the ceiling before disappearing through an open chimney.

Standing on a small table next to the settle was an old fashioned radio which was wired to an accumulator that stood on the floor of faded red flagstone. These were well worn in certain areas denoting the passage of many footsteps over the years.

Against the back wall of the kitchen, next to the doorway leading into the back room, stood a huge black dresser whose shelves were filled with a multitude of china plates, bowls, cups and dishes of all colours, shapes, patterns and sizes.

Looking across at my sister, I was not surprised to see she was getting upset by all the questions bombarded at her, for we had been brought up to understand that it was rude to ask personal questions. She looked vulnerable and younger than her years as she stood, head down, surrounded by strangers. Rene wore her wavy brown hair rather too short; her pink cheeks were bright red and her blue eyes seemed about to shed a tear. She had outgrown the unbuttoned cardigan that she was wearing over her light summer frock, the skirt of which was too short for her long legs. Rene was at that awkward period in a girl's life, just prior to changing from a child into a beautiful woman. I moved closer to her.

Mrs Ladd came to our rescue saying it was time for bed, and as all the people slowly left they each came up to us to offer words of comfort and assurance before wishing us goodnight. We learned later that they had all been waiting for hours, curious to see who Mrs Ladd might bring home to Dolrannog. They were really very kind people, but we had not had enough time to realise that.

We were too tired to feel hungry, but we did enjoy a mug of fresh creamy milk. Mrs Ladd was ready to take us up the stairs but Rene said we needed to go to the toilet and to brush our teeth. Mrs Ladd took us outside through the back door and, pointing to the mountain, told us there were plenty of places up there we could use as a toilet, and not to worry about cleaning our teeth as it was so late. She then disappeared inside the house leaving Rene and I looking at each other in astonishment.

I could see my sister starting to get upset again. She had promised our mother that we would have a wash and clean our teeth each night before bed and it seemed that the promise would be broken on our first night. Though feeling far from happy myself, I was more worried about Rene as she was highly strung and had already suffered a nervous breakdown caused by swotting for scholarship before the war. I tried to cheer her up as we walked away from the farmhouse.

The small field we were in sloped steeply towards the mountain on whose peak the moon was briefly balancing. On the other side and out of sight was the village, almost surrounded by ocean from which a cool breeze was blowing. We stood bemused watching the moon as it continued its journey across the sky and wondered if our parents were watching it too. We were immediately engulfed by a wave of home sickness which caused a flood of tears to fall down our cheeks. This somehow helped to relieve some of the strain we had been under since leaving home. Then a call from the house reminded us of the reason for our being outside.

Turning away from my sister I found a hedgerow that needed watering and I had almost completed my task when I heard hoof beats approaching from the next field. This was followed by a loud crashing noise as a bull thrust his head through the hedge inches from my left ear and let out a mighty bellow. Still in a state of disarray I took off like a rocket, closely followed by Rene.

Bursting through the back door, we were safely inside the farmhouse in seconds and telling the family of our fright. Their response was to burst into laughter before explaining that Dolrannog did not even possess a bull and that there were only calves in the adjacent field who, being hand fed, were very tame and always looking for more food. I made up my mind to check it out in the morning; it had certainly looked like a bull to me.

Saying we would get to know everyone in the morning, when we were not so tired, Mrs Ladd led the way upstairs carrying a lighted candle and, bidding the rest of the family goodnight, we followed her.

At the top of the stairs was a narrow landing, on each side of which a door opened into a bedroom, one at each end of the house. In the middle another door opened into a tiny bedroom which was situated above the stairwell. The roof almost sloped down to the floor. From this open door we looked across at our little window which was situated above the porch. One half of the room was completely taken up by a large old fashioned double bed leaving just enough space for a modest chest of drawers on which Mrs Ladd placed the candle in its holder.

Moving to the doorway, she then made us aware of the serious risk of fire by pointing out that all the walls, floors and ceilings, and also the stairs, were made of wood which had become tinder dry over the years. Mrs Ladd then told us we had to blow the candle out before we got into bed in case we fell asleep and forgot. She told us to use the chamber pot under the bed if we needed 'to go' in the night, not to wander around in the dark and then, assuring us of our safety, she wished us a good night's sleep.

It took us less than a minute to unpack our few clothes and put them in the drawers of the chest and place our unused toilet items on the top next to the candle. Rene blew out the candle as we prepared to put our unwashed bodies to bed, turning away modestly as she put on her nightie and I put on my pyjamas. We then knelt together and said our prayers which took a little longer than at home but at least we were able to keep one promise to our parents.

I was first to climb into bed, being closest to the wall and I promptly sank into the feather mattress. Rene followed, also sinking down and creating a ridge between us. This formed a natural barrier and kept us apart so that we never touched, not even when Rene was sobbing silently next to me, which she did for many nights to come. Although the night was cool we soon became far too hot, and on adjusting the bedclothes we found that as well as several blankets, we also had a thick eiderdown stuffed with real feathers, and a patchwork quilt.

Although we were physically exhausted our brains were far too active for sleep to come quickly. We heard our new family climb the stairs as they too made their way to bed, still talking quietly. We could hear every sound they made, and we became more aware of the matchwood thinness of the dividing walls. We also realised that if we could hear them then they could hear us. Sleep became even more difficult in our new surroundings as their heavy breathing turned into snoring.

Except for when Rene attended a school camp on the Isle of Wight, we had never before been separated from our parents and I couldn't help but wonder where they might be now. The Germans could already have invaded our home. I found it hard to believe that only one day had passed since we had left. Rene was restless and I could hear her sobbing quietly and remembering my father's words I had to try hard not to cry with her. Eventually, sleep came but only to form a backdrop for dreams, dreams of home and the happy times we had had before the war when we were still together as a family should be.

I awoke in shock and it took several seconds to remember where I was and the events of the previous day. I looked at Rene, who was lying on her back staring at the wooden ceiling, her eyes puffy from crying. This brought on another bout of home sickness but my curiosity prevailed as I heard noises outside. Climbing over Rene, I made my way to the window through which bright sunlight was streaming in. The thick walls formed a deep recess making the low window sill plenty wide enough for me to sit on.

Looking out I saw Mrs Ladd by the little gate at the front of the house shouting to someone who was out of sight. Still dressed in black she now wore a beret on her head and a navy blue pinafore, but what intrigued me most was the clip-clop sound as she walked up the short cobblestone path and into the house. Mrs Ladd was wearing clogs which were common to most of the farming community.

I continued to look out the window while Rene dressed. Directly across from us on the other side of the valley was another farm. Its matchbox like buildings were whitewashed and in good repair with the fields divided neatly into squares and oblongs like the patchwork on our quilt. They seemed greener and free of stone, unlike this side of the valley. Cows were lying contentedly chewing their cud. Above the fields were rolling hills, on which hundreds of sheep roamed, stretching to the horizon.

Wisps of smoke rising above small clumps of trees provided evidence of other hidden farmlets or cottages. The scene was one of peace and great beauty; it was hard to think about war.

After getting dressed we decided to make the bed. This proved quite difficult as the bed was too heavy to move and my side was jammed against the wall. The chamber pot was still empty, a fact which caused us to hurry downstairs. Remembering our experience of the night before we had decided to leave our toiletries on top of the chest of drawers until we found out where to use them.

Mrs Ladd was attending to the stove as we entered the kitchen and our greetings were rather hurried as we made for the back door. After watering my favourite hedge, I spent several minutes inspecting the adjoining field, in which there were several calves of different colours and sizes. I had to admit though, that none of them in any way resembled a bull! I decided the moonlight had been playing tricks on me.

Back in the farmhouse we watched Mrs Ladd pouring boiling water into a large china teapot. The water was boiled in a huge iron kettle suspended from a chain over the fire. Both teapot and kettle were covered in soot. At this moment, Megan came through the back door carrying a large jug of cream. The jug looked well used with its yellow enamel paint badly chipped. After putting the cream in the pantry she entered the kitchen and greeted us most warmly. Megan was several years older than Rene. She was also heavier than her but no taller.

She wore her wavy hair quite short. It was light brown, the same colour as her eyes and though she wore glasses, this in no way detracted from the light of love and kindness that they reflected. She wore a light summer dress and a floral apron. Her skin was soft and creamy, and her bare legs made the ugly clogs she was wearing seem incongruous as she clip-clopped across the flagstones. We came to love Megan and she and Rene formed a particularly strong friendship.

It was Megan who took us aside and told us that Dolrannog had no bathroom or toilet. We didn't have a proper bathroom at home either and the bathtub was kept under the kitchen table. But we were non-plussed about the lack of a toilet. From then on, we made a note of suitable places, especially where large dock leaves could be found, and we quickly learned to keep clear of thistles and nettles! It was not too much of a worry in the summer but we could foresee trouble in the winter. We hoped the war would be over before then!

The farmhouse was set into the slope of the mountain which brought the roof at the back closer to the ground. There were no windows at the back of the house, only the door, from which a few steps eased the way up the rise to a gate in the wall of the farmyard. In the corner, where the wall joined the house, was a small rock pool. This was reached from the back door over three steps cut from solid slabs of slate. These were always wet and slippery as water from the mountain stream fell continuously into the pond through an earthenware pipe. Another pipe directed the overflow of water under the wall into the farmyard, much to the delight of the ducks.

Megan handed me some soap and I gingerly went down the wet, slippery steps; I wanted a wash not a bath! I was wearing sandals and the water splashed my feet, and though it was summer, it felt icy cold. Megan told us that in winter all the water would freeze to form an ice grotto. After a quick splash I went inside for breakfast, I was starving. Mrs Ladd was still by the fire but now cooking bacon and eggs in a large cast iron frying pan, which was as black as the soot. This did not stop me from drooling as my nose detected the most tantalising odour.

Sunlight shone through the small window but it was not enough to dispel the gloom from the large kitchen. Outside, the cows were meandering down the lane returning to their pastures after milking. Neither the barking of the dogs nor the shouts from Benny had the slightest effect on them as they continued, in strict sequence, at their own leisurely pace.

On entering through the open front door Mr Ladd greeted me in his gentle manner. He took off his hat, which looked as if it had once belonged to a scarecrow, and sat down at the table. His thin grey hair was receding and he looked tired and old. He had gaps in his teeth but the dominant feature was a large wart under his left eye.

Although the day was warm, he was wearing a collarless flannel shirt and an old black suit, complete with waistcoat, which had seem many better days. However, nothing in his appearance could detract from the overriding air of dignity he portrayed.

Benny was in complete contrast to his father as he came bursting in. Seating himself at the table, he swallowed his first forkful almost before Mrs Ladd had time to put his bacon and eggs in front of him.

Benny was wearing a tweed cap perched at an impossible angle over one ear. At a word from his father, the cap was thrown off to reveal straight black hair, slicked back and kept in place with hair oil. His features were drawn and pale, but the open necked shirt he was wearing with sleeves rolled up, showed strong and muscular arms. He was a man at seventeen years of age.

Megan and Rene entered the room chatting away to each other. Mrs Ladd said she had not cooked anything for our breakfast, not knowing what time we would be awake or what we would like to eat. She added that as soon as the men were fed she would then feed us.

I couldn't help staring at Benny as he demolished his breakfast. He loaded his fork with thick chunks of crispy bacon and piled eggs onto bread and butter. He washed it all down with a mug of tea. My mouth was watering and I was starving.

After a second mug of tea and with cigarettes alight the men finally left the table to do their chores. Megan cleared away then set places at the table for Rene and me before leaving us alone with Mrs Ladd.

Mesmerised, my eyes stayed focused on the bacon

hanging from the ceiling in order to make sure that Mrs Ladd knew what I wanted for breakfast. (Bacon had been a Sunday morning treat at home.) Taking a long stick from the corner by the dresser Mrs Ladd deftly unhooked a fletch of bacon from the ceiling. The brown skin outside was dry and smelt smoky but where it had been cut into the thick layer of fat was as white as snow. Under it the meat looked as pink and succulent as a fresh mushroom. I watched in awe as Mrs Ladd proceeded to cut off thick slices with her large carving knife and my eyes followed her to the fire where she placed them on the hot frying pan. They were soon a lovely golden colour and after turning them, she cracked a few eggs alongside the rashers. While these were cooking she sliced and buttered more bread for us.

Sitting at the table with knife and fork in hand, I lost no time in attacking my bacon as soon as Mrs Ladd had put the plate in front of me. I attempted to cut the thickest piece in half only to watch in horror as it shot off the plate and slid across the table. Having put it back on my plate I did manage to cut a piece off on my third attempt. I then, gingerly, put it in my mouth. After about sixty chews it still had not changed shape nor substance; it was as tough as an old boot. But that was only part of my disappointment because it was also so salty that my mouth dried up. There was no way I could swallow it! Rene had turned a bright pink so I knew that she was in the same predicament.

Luckily, Mrs Ladd had turned away from us and was filling her cup from the teapot keeping warm on the stove. My sister watched in amazement as I spat the bacon out of my mouth, picked up the rest from my plate and stuffed it all in my pocket. Then, keeping an eye on Mrs Ladd, I leaned over and grabbed all of Rene's bacon and shoved that in my pocket too!

With a cup of tea in hand Mrs Ladd came over to see how we were getting on with our breakfast and was most surprised to see that we had no bacon left on our plates. She remarked on how quickly we had eaten it and how much we must have enjoyed it. She added that we had probably never had bacon like it before; a remark with which Rene and I could honestly agree. We filled up on the eggs and bread and butter before excusing ourselves and going outside.

Lil, the black and white sheep dog, was lying under her bench in the porch, so I emptied my now greasy pocket and watched with relief as she demolished the evidence in one gulp. I had made a friend for life! This proved to be quite embarrassing, however, because from then on, every time she saw me, she insisted on putting her nose into my pocket! As we slowly adjusted to our new environment we acquired many of the Welsh ways and we even grew to like the home cured bacon.

Chapter 3

DOLRANNOG

On looking around us at our new surroundings in bright
sunlight, our first impression was one of dismay. The house
was situated about twenty yards inside the main gate,
facing directly down the lane. It looked solid with a
chimney at each end, a porch in the middle with a window
on either side and three small windows above. The white
paint on the window frames was peeling. A low stone wall
enclosed a minute front garden which was entered through
an iron gate to a cobblestone path. Nothing grew in the
garden because the chickens found easy access and
continually checked it out.

The house itself formed one side of the farmyard, which
was square and sloped away from the mountain. Along the
other side was a long low building, obviously old, but in
reasonable repair with the walls whitewashed and the door
frames painted with red lead. The upper end provided
stabling for the horses and in the middle section was the
barn. This was separated from the cowshed by a low
internal wall which facilitated the feeding of the cows.
Over the cowshed was a loft, reached by a ladder, where a
small window at floor level gave a hint of light. A door in

the back wall of the barn gave direct access to the hay-guard where the hay stacks stood. Also against the back wall was an ancient water wheel, seized with rust, its wooden paddles rotting. It had obviously not turned in years.

There were no windows in the cowshed which could accommodate a dozen animals, six on each side. It had a cement floor which made it easy to hose down and outside the door was a large dung heap which was constantly scratched over by the chickens.

Across the top of the yard was another long, low building whose roof sagged and with its doors awry. It seemed to have been derelict for many years.

Forming the bottom of the square, a low stone wall swept from the front gate to another gate at the end of the cowshed where the lane continued to the next farm. These gates were normally left open. Behind the wall was a row of tall trees and set into the wall were two wooden gates leading to two pig sties. These gates were left open and were only closed if a sow was in residence giving birth to a litter.

It was the smallest building that was the most noticeable though, because it was built from wood and corrugated iron while everything else was built from solid rock. It was the size of a sentry box and looked like an outside toilet but carried the grand title of 'the dairy'. It was big enough to hold four churns, a couple of buckets and one person on its cement floor. High on the back wall was a shelf on which stood a large steel bowl; this was filled with milk directly from the cows. Suspended from the shelf and directly under the tap in the bowl was a milk cooler, which looked very much like an old fashioned wash board. Cold water constantly flowed through the steel cooler on the inside to cool the milk that flowed on the outside, through a filter and into a churn. This was Megan's domain. It was not an easy job as it involved a lot of lifting and everything had to be kept spotless. In winter there was no need to cool the milk, only filter it.

For some reason the dairy was situated at the furthest point from the cowshed, next to the derelict building. This caused a lot of trips between the two places carrying heavy buckets of milk. The task was made worse by the wet uneven ground and in winter by the rain and darkness.

There were only two taps in Dolrannog, one in the cowshed and the other in the dairy. Plumbing was most basic, in fact almost non existent. In the top corner of the yard, near the dairy, water continually flowed into a big brass tub by way of an earthenware pipe protruding from the wall. This was for the animals to drink. It was fed by the same stream that delivered our washing water to the back of the house. The flow from the two pipes was regulated quite simply by kicking the sod or a few stones into the path of the stream, making a dam to divert the water where required. Even in summer, the excess water flowed across the yard to disappear under the wall by the pig sty and eventually find its way to the river in the valley below. Ducks of all shapes, sizes and colours continually probed the muddy bottom of the stream while ducklings practised their swimming in close attendance. In some shade by the stables turkeys rested out of the sun, while a large angry looking gobbler stood guard, his wattles shining bright red.

Apart from chickens of every breed there were also

guinea fowl and bantams wandering around the yard or scratching over the dung heap. Mother hens fussed over their baby chicks while a rooster would occasionally try to outrun a frightened pullet.

A gaggle of geese, who had been grazing in the next field, now entered the farmyard in a most noisy manner. All talking at once, they were led by the head gander who was putting on quite a show as he conducted them to water. His wings were flapping wildly, his neck extended and his head was only inches from the ground. Hissing loudly he came towards me. I took off with Rene besides me. Fortunately Benny had just finished cleaning the cowshed and was standing at the door with a broom in his hands. In fright, I ran straight to him by the shortest route, which was over the dung heap. Taking no notice as my sandalled feet sank deeply into the morning's fresh dung, I leapt desperately through the cowshed door, closely followed by Rene. The dogs ran from the porch to see what all the fuss was about and joined Benny in sending the geese away. I couldn't help but notice how brutal the big dog was, and even Benny had trouble controlling him when he grabbed a goose by the neck.

Mrs Ladd and Megan, attracted by the noise, appeared from inside the house just as Mr Ladd arrived back with the empty milk churns on a horse and cart. They all looked at me as I left the cowshed followed by Rene, who was holding her nose. Looking at me, Benny burst into uncontrollable laughter and everyone else joined in.

Looking down at my legs I saw that they were covered in dung up to my knees and as it dried, it looked as though I was wearing long brown socks. The pervading odour had

35

nothing to do with violets! Having been really frightened by the gander, I now felt miserable standing there being laughed at. At least Rene wasn't laughing at me and I tried to put on a brave face.

It was Megan who came to my aid. She shouted something in Welsh to the men who unloaded the churns into the dairy and unharnessed the horse. She then led me by the hand to the spout by the back door. Handing me a scrubbing brush and a bar of carbolic soap she watched me clean myself up. By the time I was presentable again my legs had changed from a chocolate brown to a delicate shade of pink and my sandals were becoming more uncomfortable as the edges curled up as they dried.

Having passed inspection by Megan, I was allowed into the house where Mrs Ladd was in her usual position next to the stove, but this time she was cooking pancakes on the huge black griddle plate over the fire. I watched as she deftly spooned the mixture onto the hotplate and almost instantly turned it over before lifting the now cooked pancake onto a warm tray. She seemed to be able to cook about twenty at one time, at an amazing pace, all perfect in shape and size and all cooked to the same light brown colour. They were then topped off with a thin smear of farm butter while still warm. Mrs Ladd kept up production until everyone, including me, was satisfied.

After emptying their mugs of tea, and ritually rolling their cigarettes, the men went outside again and we helped Megan clear away. While washing up in a large enamel bowl in the back room, Megan told us this was where we could give ourselves a proper wash in hot water. She explained that by placing the bowl on the floor and standing in it, we could wash ourselves all over with a flannel.

The back room was small and sparsely furnished with a table and benches of pine, kept white with constant scrubbing. In the corner by the back door stood a butter churn on its trestle, and in the opposite corner by the kitchen door was an old fashioned, black, iron cheese press. Between the two another door led to the pantry which extended the rest of the way along the back of the house and was a veritable Aladdin's cave. Solid slate troughs contained various cuts of meat hidden under a mountain of salt. On slate shelves, round cheeses stood amid squares of butter. Bowls of thick cream stood alongside fresh eggs and a myriad of stone pots and glazed jars were filled with fruit and pickled vegetables, all prepared from secret formulas. Two wooden beer kegs stood on trestles at the far end. Megan ushered me out, interrupting my thoughts about future secret explorations. Following Megan outside into the warm sun, we realised how efficient the method of construction and the positioning of the pantry was in keeping everything so cool.

Megan said it was time to feed the chickens and collect the eggs and we followed her to the barn where she filled a wooden handled dipper with corn from one of the many sacks piled against the wall. Standing in the middle of the yard, she called to the chickens in a high pitched voice. Some were already gathered around her waiting impatiently, while others came running with flapping wings making a lot of noise. The dogs came running out, joining in and barking madly but a couple of quick commands from Megan had them slinking back to the shade of the porch.

Rene and I helped throw the corn around, trying to be fair by throwing it closer to the weakest and slowest. Order returned as the feeding frenzy subsided to a desultory picking; obviously, none had been starving there was too much natural feed around. We watched for a while, fascinated by the multitude of colours of the many different breeds which gave a kaleidoscopic effect to the normally dull farmyard.

There were no chicken runs or hen houses at Dolrannog. All the birds had the run of the farm and had to find their own places of safety to lay their eggs and to perch at night. Being easy prey for foxes on the ground and vulnerable to attacks from larger birds of prey from the air, only the most cunning survived and so a constant game of hide and seek took place as the hens sought better hiding places for their nests.

We started by looking in the barn, which was none too tidy. There were piles of empty sacks and rows of full ones, and loose hay and straw had been allowed to gather in the corners. This all provided first class accommodation for broody hens. Megan pointed out the likely places and we were soon placing fresh eggs in the dipper. If a hen was still on the nest it was not disturbed and regardless of the number of eggs collected from a nest, one was always left behind. Megan explained to us that as the hens couldn't count, they would keep coming back to the nest providing it was not empty.

Leaving the barn by the back door we proceeded to search round the hay stacks and then the stable, by which time the dipper was nearly full. Megan ignored the derelict building even though hens were entering and leaving, and she warned us once again never to go inside as it was very dangerous. Megan seemed quite satisfied with the number of eggs she was now putting in the pantry but I was sure I could have found a lot more!

After a lunch of vegetable soup and bread and cheese, Rene said we had to write to our parents who had no idea where we were. Mrs Ladd said we could sit at the table by the little window where there was the most light and Rene went upstairs to fetch the pad and envelopes that our Mother had packed for us. Mrs Ladd carefully spelt out our new address, explaining that the name of the farm, Dolrannog Uchaf, meant upper divided meadows in English. She also confirmed that Fishguard, where we had finally left the train, was our closest town with the next closest being Cardigan about twelve miles in the opposite direction. At least our parents would now be able to find us on a map.

As I sat chewing my pencil wondering what to say in my first letter home, Rene instructed me not to write anything that would cause more worry for our parents and not to ask for anything. This dampened any enthusiasm I may have had to become a writer because I had already compiled a list of things I considered to be necessary for my survival on the mountain, with a pair of clogs having priority. So, on completion, my first missive resembled more a short catalogue of farm animals than a letter from an absent son to his loving parents.

Mrs Ladd could not contain her curiosity about what we had said in our letters which didn't worry me at all and I read mine out loud. Rene was determined to guard her privacy and, with lips clamped tightly together, she placed the letters in one envelope and sealed it. Tears came to her eyes as she wrote the address and my spirits sank as I too, became aware of the possibility that our home and parents might no longer exist! We could have been bombed or invaded by the Germans. During our own upheaval of the last twenty four hours we had almost forgotten that there was a war raging somewhere. Mrs Ladd tried to give us some comfort by saying we would find out what was going on when we listened to the news on the radio, and we could post our letters the next day.

Rene was upstairs putting away the letter and writing materials when Megan called to ask if we would like to accompany her down the lane to fetch the cows for milking. I went outside to join her and the dogs who were waiting patiently. Lil immediately came to me her tail wagging, trying to get her nose into my trouser pocket. I pushed her away and gave her a pat.

As we walked down the lane Megan again warned us about making pets of the dogs, reminding us that they were working dogs. Lil was a typical black and white Welsh sheep dog; Rover was twice her size, brown in colour and looked more like a wolf than a dog. He was Benny's hunting dog but it was also his job to keep the foxes at bay. The dogs were never fed but had to forage for themselves, which was not much of a hardship there being plenty of rabbits about.

I couldn't help thinking about Sally, our fox terrier. She kept our coal cellar free of rats and always had some Snapps dog biscuits in her bowl. At the beginning of the war our father had given her to a friend to look after and I couldn't help wondering if I would ever see her again.

We came to a gate in a field where the cows were already lined up and waiting. With the opening of the gate, the dogs made a desultory attempt to hurry the cows through but were completely ignored, so they ran off to check the hedgerow for fugitive rabbits. Keeping to their own leisurely pace with full udders swinging, the cows made their way back to the farm. There were about twenty head of cattle of various sizes and colours and each one had its own place in the line according to seniority. Only about half were milking cows; the remainder were young heifers in various stages of pregnancy.

It was a peaceful and orderly scene as we followed the cows up the lane. We enjoyed being with Megan who explained to us the workings of the farm. It was also music to our ears just to listen and to be spoken to in English without Welsh taking over, which we were finding to be most frustrating.

As we approached the farm the orderliness of the procession was disrupted up ahead by one cow that had started to bellow and push herself to the front of the line. The cows ahead of her resented the move and she was kept in place with some well aimed prods from their horns.

Megan explained to us that the fractious cow had given birth to a male calf a few days ago. It had been taken from her and placed with the other calves in their field next to the house to be sold as veal in a few days time. We noticed milk dripping from the cow's teats as it finally burst into the farmyard and made for the gate to the calves' field. Here, all the calves had now gathered, and were trying to push their heads through the gate, calling to their mothers.

The mother cow was frantically licking her baby who was in danger of being crushed.

While all this was happening the milking cows were entering the cowshed in a most orderly fashion and the heifers stood around in the farmyard contentedly chewing their cud as they waited to be returned to their field.

The mother cow was loath to leave its calf again and had no desire to enter the cowshed. At that moment Mrs Ladd appeared with a heavy stick and set about the unfortunate animal and, what with all our shouting and shoving and the dogs barking and snapping at its heels, the poor beast finally sought refuge in its own bail in the cowshed.

Rene and I were a bit upset and felt sorry for the little calf who was still crying out for its mother. Megan tried to cheer us up by explaining that half of the milk would be left after the milking of its mother and the calf would be allowed to drink it. The other calves, being older, would be fed on formula because they could also graze. Megan said we could watch her milking but we would have to be quiet.

It was peaceful in the cowshed where Mr Ladd and Benny had already started the milking. Mrs Ladd returned to the house to prepare the evening meal. She only milked if she had to. Her shape was not conducive to sitting on a three legged milking stool for too long.

Megan picked up a stool and bucket and gave a cow a slap on the rump. It obligingly moved to one side and Megan placed the stool in position and sat down, holding the bucket between her knees and resting her head against the cow's flank. Speaking quietly to the cow, she grasped two of its teats and started pulling and squeezing in a rhythmic way. At first only a trickle of milk appeared but this turned into a steady stream as the cow relaxed, and Megan joined in with Mr Ladd and Benny in performing a six handed concerto.

The shed could hold twelve cows, but on this night there were only ten to be milked since one was about to calve and another had gone dry. It was warm and relaxing inside and the rhythmic sound of the milking created an almost hypnotic effect and I was nearly asleep on my feet when Benny moved to the cow nearest me. He soon had the milk flowing in a steady stream into his bucket creating a creamy head of foam. Then, placing a finger on his lips to signify silence he called me to him. In a whisper he told me to open my mouth and close my eyes if I wanted a big surprise. Of course I did, and was immediately hit in the face by a jet of warm milk, some of which went into my mouth and some up my nose. I let out a scream of surprise then burst into laughter which was cut short as I realised in horror that the once peaceful cowshed had turned into a scene from Bedlam.

Ten cows leapt into the air simultaneously and were only restrained from evacuating the building, en masse, by their tie ropes. Milking stools were overturned, depositing their occupants onto the wet concrete floor, where they performed a grotesque ballet as they desperately tried to keep the buckets upright in order not to spill the milk. One cow had a back foot in a bucket and appeared to be trying to churn the milk into butter.

Against all the rules, the dogs came charging in to investigate the rumpus and managed a few quick licks of spilt milk before beating a hasty retreat under an avalanche of well aimed clogs. Mrs Ladd made a brief appearance in the doorway, pulling her apron over her head before praying to God and beating a hasty retreat to the house.

It took quite a while for things to return to normal during which time Mr Ladd had quite a lot to say to Benny, and although I couldn't understand the words, I had no trouble in grasping the meaning of what he was saying. Megan came to my rescue by putting the blame on Benny, but I still received quite a talking to from Mr Ladd regarding appropriate behaviour around animals.

At the end of milking we helped Megan carry the buckets across the farmyard to the tiny dairy where we were relieved to learn that although the milk production was down, it was not catastrophically so.

The atmosphere was rather strained that evening as Rene and I sat patiently waiting to listen to the news before going to bed. All eyes were focused on the old pendulum wall clock which was situated directly above the wireless. The chimes had ceased to work many years before and now, when the minute hand reached the hour, the noise it made sounded as if it was having an asthma attack.

Everyone became silent when it was time to switch on the wireless. They sat staring at it as if they were trying, not only to hear what it was about to say, but also to visualise it. We heard the pips and as the news reader started to read out his bulletin I cried out in dismay and disbelief as he did so in Welsh. I was quickly told to be quiet.

We sat in utter frustration trying to learn which way the war was going and if the Germans had invaded England yet. All we had to go on was the tone of their brief exclamations.

After the news had finished, the family discussed what they had just heard before one of them translated for us – not an easy task I'm sure when one bears in mind the fact that many of the places mentioned had probably not been heard of before the war.

On this night we were assured that the Germans had not invaded England but the bombing was still continuing. Obviously we would not be going home yet, and it was two sad children who said their prayers that night. I lay thinking about our first full day; not much had gone right for me. I didn't want to be on a farm and I felt my sister sobbing quietly next to me. I thought about father, screwed my eyes tight shut and waited for sleep.

Chapter 4

OUT AND ABOUT

We didn't linger over breakfast the next morning. Without asking us what we would like to eat, Mrs Ladd presented us with a boiled egg and some bread and butter. From then on eggs became our staple breakfast food, fried scrambled or boiled.

We found Megan in her tiny dairy watching the last drops of milk flow down the cooler before disappearing through the filter into the churn. She then proceeded to hose everything down, using a copious amount of water. She told us that the water came from a well a few hundred yards up the rise. Amazingly, although the ocean was three miles away and the well was about one thousand feet above sea level, the water in the well still rose and fell with the tide. The well never ran dry and the water was always fresh and cool, a fact that Rene and I agreed on after tasting it.

Across the yard, Benny was hosing out the cowshed after adding more manure to the pile outside, which was now being scratched over by the hens. The ducks were splashing in the water that flowed across the yard from the dairy and objected strongly when they were forced to scatter as Mr Ladd appeared on the scene leading a horse and cart. On this was loaded the four milk churns ready to rendezvous with the milk truck at the end of the lane.

Rene and Megan had already gone back to the house when Mr Ladd asked me if I would like to go with him for a ride. I immediately accepted his offer but soon came to regret doing so. The cart, or float as it was called, looked to be quite comfortable, having springs and proper tyres on its two wheels. The four churns were loaded at the front and secured by a rope to stop them sliding about.

I climbed up next to Mr Ladd who was standing in the small space behind the churns. With a shake of the reins he started the horse on its leisurely journey. He had no difficulty in keeping his balance, even though the float sloped backwards and swayed from side to side in rhythm with the horse's gait. I couldn't keep my balance but I couldn't sit down as the wood was dry and splintery. I survived by squatting and holding on to a churn which didn't seem to want to stay in its place. Apart from the occasional rattle of the churns we made little noise since the track in the centre of the lane had been broken up by countless horses, hooves and formed a soft powdery surface. Even so, the dogs came out barking from the neighbouring farm, only to lose interest on seeing a daily routine occurrence.

On reaching the road we loaded the churns on to a rough wooden stand and I held the reins as Turpin grazed along the hedgerow. I was glad to stretch my legs and get rid of the pins and needles which had developed during the ride. Mr Ladd rested against the stand smoking a cigarette as a hawk hovered high overhead. My thoughts turned homeward as I became enveloped by the peacefulness of my surroundings. I still couldn't believe that the world was at war.

The rattle of an engine brought me back to reality as an old brown truck pulled up alongside the stand. It smelt hot and its petrol fumes polluted the pristine mountain air as the men exchanged the full churns for clean empty ones. After a brief conversation in Welsh, during which their glances towards me suggested that I was the main subject, the two men parted. With a crunch from the gearbox and more fumes from the exhaust, the truck pulled away with a jerk causing the churns to rattle in tune with the engine.

Although the cart was not heavily laden with just the four empty churns now Mr Ladd chose to walk awhile as the trip home was uphill. My joining him, gave us a good chance to talk, and it was indeed a great pleasure for me to be heard and spoken to without anyone else present to interrupt. He answered all my questions carefully and explained to me the workings of the farm in great detail. To me, Mr Ladd became the grandfather I had never had, full of patience, wisdom and kindness.

As I helped to unhook the cart and then leading Turpin to be unharnessed in the stable, I felt a little less like a fish out of water, knowing I had a friend in Mr Ladd. We went into the house for morning tea and were met by Rene and Megan who were coming out. Rene told me she was going with Megan to post our letter, a task which enabled her to keep another promise to our mother. I decided to go with them. I hastily drank my mug of cold milk and with a cheese sandwich in my hand I soon caught them up down the lane. Having already walked over a mile and a half uphill with Mr Ladd, I almost changed my mind when Megan told me the journey would be almost six miles. But I didn't feel tired and the day was perfect so I decided to go with them and again had the opportunity of joining in a conversation without hearing a word of Welsh. As usual, the dogs from the neighbouring farm rushed at us and I stayed very close to Megan who told us to just keep walking and to ignore them. That was not easy to do as I could feel their hot breath on my naked legs. A man whistled and the dogs ran off but no conversation took place. Apparently, there was no friendship between the two farms, for what reason I was never told.

We left the lane half way along where the hedgerows finished and followed a track down the mountainside to a stone wall behind which there were two cottages. The first one belonged to Mair, Megan's sister who, Megan said, we would visit on our return. At the second cottage an ancient couple were waiting for us at their front gate, giving us no option but to stop and talk. They were dressed in the obligatory black clothing down the front of which remnants of many past meals formed an interesting pattern. Rene and I took a couple of paces backwards when it became obvious that they possessed more gaps than teeth as they simultaneously bombarded Megan with questions in Welsh.

The conversation obviously centred around us and seemed to go on forever, before Megan could break away. She told us that the couple had never been away from the village and spoke no English, something that was not uncommon amongst the older generation. Megan also told us that nobody she knew in the district had ever left Wales and this helped to explain everyone's curiosity at our arrival.

Passing through a five bar gate we followed a short lane to the road where a grey stone house stood facing us. It was made distinctive by a few small signs advertising cigarettes and various brands of tea proclaiming the fact that, like so many other cottages, the front parlour had been converted into a shop. The house was called Ty'n Rhos and was the home of a middle aged spinster, Miss James, who was known by the name of Miss James, Ty'n Rhos. She appeared in the doorway, dressed in black, and invited us in.

The room's one small window let in little light and it took a while for my eyes to adjust to the gloom and see what was on display. I was disappointed to learn that Miss James stocked only the most basic commodities but as my vision cleared I did see a few peppermints and some bulls'-eyes in the jars standing on the shelves behind the counter.

As usual, I had stepped back to let my sister answer the inevitable questions from Miss James, who then turned and discussed Rene's reply in Welsh with Megan. At first Megan tried to persevere to keep the conversation going in English, but she too slipped back into speaking Welsh which after all was her first language. Once again, Rene and I could only stand and wait.

When we were finally able to make our departure Miss James gave Rene and I a peppermint each. Mine didn't last very long as I could never resist the urge to chew instead of suck, whereas Rene could make hers last for ever. Heading towards the valley we passed a small wood. A ruined cottage was occupied by Hughie the Hermit, so Megan told us, and was just visible through the undergrowth. On seeing the concerned look on Rene's face Megan added that even though he looked wild, with his long hair and untrimmed beard, he was really quite timid.

The road now twisted and turned as we came to a stone bridge across the river. The road was too narrow for even two small cars to pass and the bridge was even narrower. I wondered how much room there was to spare when the milk truck passed over it. At the entrance to the valley the road forked with one way following the river and twisting and turning along the floor of the valley while the other climbed and wound its way along the top of the valley.

At this point, a red letter box stood like a sentry outside a small cottage on whose front door was a sign saying Post Office. A few chickens scratched around the front and a solitary cow grazed in the field behind the cottage. The inevitable black and white dog barked a warning before wagging its tail in welcome after deciding we were not a threat to its domain.

Again, it took time for our eyes to adjust but all there was to see as we entered the tiny front room was a wooden counter with an ancient set of brass scales standing on it. Some war time posters were stuck on the walls urging people to save and not give away secrets to the enemy. I wondered what secrets there were to tell in this part of the world, and I certainly hadn't seen anyone with any money to spare.

An old couple emerged from an open doorway leading from their kitchen and we were introduced to Mr and Mrs James, the Post. He spoke some English but she had no knowledge of the language at all. At least this prevented them from asking us all the usual questions and they directed their queries to Megan, while we waited impatiently to post our letter.

Eventually Rene handed it to the Postmaster who gave it a microscopic examination on both sides before handing it to the Postmistress to double-check. It was then put on the scales and after the correct weight was ascertained and stamps of the correct value affixed it was handed back to Rene for posting in the red letter box outside. Megan cleverly managed to evacuate the post office without committing us to a session of tea drinking, though we were grateful for a mug of cold water on such a warm day.

We were quiet as we retraced our steps. Megan walked a little behind us, giving us time and privacy to discuss the fate of our letter home. She was a lovely warm and sensitive person who seemed to understand all our needs. Rene and I wondered if our parents were still together. Dad could have been posted anywhere and Mother could have gone to any one of our aunts, leaving the house empty with our letter sitting on the front door mat. Worse, our home could have been bombed. All we could do now was wait for a reply.

When we stopped briefly by the bridge, I decided to climb down the bank to the water below. I found it to be quite shallow and Megan said there was probably an old ford there before the bridge was built. I decided to see if I could cross. The bottom was rocky but I kept my sandals on and at first had no trouble but as I reached the middle, the water was flowing more strongly and the rocks were quite large and slippery. Rene called out to me to turn back but I ignored her and the next instant found me sitting in a rock pool with freezing water up to my armpits. The worried looks on Rene and Megan's faces disappeared as I jumped up, and were replaced with peals of laughter at the sight of me as I scrambled to the bank. Megan advised me to stay in and take a bath, which I didn't find funny and I had no soap anyway! Apart from a couple of bruises and a graze I had suffered no physical damage but I must admit my pride had suffered a blow, and as we continued on our way my wet clothes became very uncomfortable and my sandals, having dried out a different shape, caused blisters to appear on my feet.

I shrank at the thought of a confrontation with Miss James, Ty'n Rhos and was relieved when she didn't appear. The old couple were still leaning over their front gate and gave me an inquisitive look as we passed by. Thankfully Megan didn't stop but just wished them a good day as we walked by and followed the track for a short distance alongside the wall, to where it ended at the gate to Waun Uchaf.

Entering Waun Uchaf felt like stepping from a desert into an oasis. The cottage, which resembled a doll's house, stood sparkling white in the sunshine. It had recently been whitewashed as had the walls that surrounded the small yard and outbuildings. All the doors and window frames boasted fresh red lead to protect them from the weather. Flowers bloomed in an abundance of varieties and colours along the front of the cottage, where a bright green creeper almost covered the porch. Fruit trees, some laden with fruit, grew at one end of the cottage. At the opposite end a vegetable garden was set out in neat rows, with the plants looking lush and green.

A black and white bitch roused herself from some shade

and welcomed us with a wagging tail but slow walk as she was heavy with milk. On realising they had been left, six almost identical black and white puppies gambolled after her, in a the game of follow my leader.

A speckled hen tried in vain to round up her dozen yellow chicks to take them to safety. The other hens just continued to peck and scratch in a nonchalant manner under the beady eye of a huge black cockerel, whose comb was bright red and full of blood, giving warning to any trespassing on his territory. Lying in the shade in a corner of the one small field contentedly chewing their cud were a pregnant heifer and a milking cow with similar black and white markings.

It was a scene of peace and beauty and we paused and thought of the war that was raging in other parts of the world. Our peace was broken by Mair shouting greetings from the doorway of the cottage as she came to meet us, carrying baby Tegwyn on her hip.

Mair was a tiny bird-like person and her movements, like her speech, were very quick even though her clogs looked far too big for her. Mair had a scarf tied over her hair and she wore glasses, whose tortoise-shell rims gave her an owlish appearance. Mona, who was about Rene's age, came behind and looked nothing like her mother, being a solid girl and more like her aunt Megan.

Initially all attention was on Tegwyn and the conversation flowed on in Welsh. We had all met before on our arrival at Dolrannog, but we had been too tired to match names to faces on that night. Mair led us into the tiny cottage where we all sat around the table, with Megan nursing the baby, and Rene and I becoming the centre of attention. Although the usual questions were asked, it was done in a sympathetic way with every one joining in and all speaking English. I could see Rene was enjoying talking to Mona.

All conversation ceased at the sound of pounding hooves as Emrys swung through the gate. Like a charioteer, he was standing upright in a float pulled by a stocky pony at almost full gallop. A sharp tug of the reins stopped the horse abruptly by the open door of the cottage, sending up a cloud of dust and chickens flying everywhere. Mair remonstrated in a shrill voice but Emrys only laughed as he jumped nimbly down from the float. Mona took Rene outside with her to hold the sweating horse who was breathing heavily. I could not understand what everyone was saying as he entered the room. Words came out of his mouth like bullets from a machine gun and he could have been speaking Welsh or English as he patted me on the head with a very dirty hand.

The baby was disturbed by the noise and started to grizzle. Taking Tegwyn from Megan, Emrys swung the baby high over his head causing Mair to cry out in alarm and take the now laughing baby from him. I took stock of Emrys as words bounced around the kitchen, the three adults all trying to talk above one another. He was thick set and had a swarthy appearance which reminded me of a gypsy. His rolled up shirt sleeves revealed strong muscular hands and arms and as he took his sweat-stained hat from his head a few silver hairs showed through his thick crop of black hair. A smile continuously played around his lips showing a perfect set of teeth when he laughed. But there was no doubt that his most outstanding attribute was his eyes, for they were the colour of violets, intense and sparkling.

A strong smell pervaded the kitchen as Emrys made short work of a cheese sandwich and a mug of tea, before rushing outside to the float where flies had started to swarm in the heat of the sun. And no wonder, since the float was loaded with rabbit traps and about fifty pairs of rabbits hanging over crude racks. Emrys climbed into the little space left in the front of the float and at a touch of the whip, the horse took off at a smart trot.

Back, inside Megan told us that Emrys was a professional rabbit catcher having contracts with most of the local farmers to trap on their land. He worked about one hundred traps, setting them at dusk and clearing them at dawn. He killed the rabbits by breaking their necks before gutting them and joining them by their back legs into pairs. Emrys was now off to the village with his night's work to deliver them to an agent who transported them to London where, not being rationed they were in much demand, especially by restaurants and hotels. Some people were having a profitable time because of the war, and judging by the grin on Emrys's face, he was one of them.

While Mair was putting food on the scrubbed table, the girls took turns in nursing Tegwyn. I declined to join in, knowing that babies were always wet or smelly and they all cried.

We were each given a bowl of boiled vegetables and there was bread and butter and cheese on the table and in the centre, Mair placed a large enamel jug. Megan asked if Rene and I liked buttermilk and we looked rather blankly at each other before I assured her that we both loved buttermilk. I received a scathing look from Rene as we watched Megan fill our mugs. Aware that I was being watched, I lifted the mug to my mouth and took a good swallow, trying not to screw my face up. To me it had a sour taste and the one thing I didn't like was sour milk. I watched Mona tip some of her buttermilk into her bowl to mash with the vegetables, and by doing the same with some of mine, and eating bread and butter at the same time, I found I had only half a mug left. Shutting my eyes, I swallowed it in one gulp and felt my stomach heave as I put my mug down with a sigh of relief. Megan remarked on how quickly I had drunk mine and I assured her that I had I enjoyed it, then watched in dismay as she refilled my mug, saying there was plenty more to be had.

As we walked back to Dolrannog my stomach continued to make squelching noises that became louder as we approached the neighbouring farm with its savage dogs, but for once they were nowhere to be seen. On reaching the cows' field, we opened the gate and waited for them to wend their way to be milked. I decided to keep away from the cowshed that evening.

Arriving back at Dolrannog we saw Mrs Ladd feeding the calves, which was done at milking time morning and night. The calves lived in the small field to the side of the house adjoining the vegetable garden, with the gate situated in the corner almost next to the front entrance of the house. This made feed time easier as it involved buckets of mixed formula having to be brought out from the kitchen. These buckets were of all shapes and sizes having been converted from tins and drums. All carried an assortment of dents and patches of rust, unlike the milk buckets kept in the dairy. Wire had been fitted for handles.

Into each bucket went a dipper of the formula which came in a sack and looked like oatmeal, followed by a dipper of boiling water from the boiler which formed half of the kitchen stove. This had no tap and the boiling water had to be ladled out after lifting back the heavy square lid. To each bucket was now added two dippers of cold water. It was then all mixed together by Mrs Ladd, using a wooden paddle, until it looked like a thin gruel.

We helped Mrs Ladd carry the buckets out to the five barred wooden gate where half a dozen calves were bawling for their feed and jostling each other for the best position. The biggest calves were fed first with Mrs Ladd somehow feeding two at a time before hitting them on the skull and forcing them to withdraw their heads to make way for the smaller ones. Rene and I had one each and were surprised at how hard we had to hold on to the bucket which they bunted as it became empty. Rene was upset when Mrs Ladd hit the calves as they kept pushing their heads through the gate asking for more, but I thought the paddle created more noise than pain and, as Mrs Ladd said, it was easy to feed one calf twice and starve another.

The last calf to be fed was the baby, only two days old, who couldn't drink so Mrs Ladd showed us what to do. Wetting her fingers in the formula she let the calf suck on them, bringing the bucket closer each time. He was reluctant to put his head in the bucket but with patience she was able to withdraw her hand and let him drink on his own. However, he became over keen and put his head in too far, filling his nostrils with the formula and pulling his head back in fright. It was Rene who, with patience, finally enticed him back for his feed. The bigger calves wandered off to graze, those too young to eat grass stood waiting for their next meal. They had a long time to wait.

The buckets had to be rinsed, the boiler had to be filled, the cows were coming out of the cowshed and it was time for the news. Rene and I offered to take the cows back. It was still daylight when we eventually said our goodnights and climbed the stairs to bed. Looking out of our tiny window we could see the little calf still standing by the gate, looking very forlorn so with a deep feeling of sympathy we included him in our prayers. Our prayers were not answered, however, and it was only a few days later that a light truck arrived and took all the male calves away. Rene and I didn't like the driver who just picked up a calf and threw it on the back of his truck. We called him Herod.

During the course of our stay we were able to learn and help to do many jobs on the farm, but were never forced and when we started attending school we had little time or energy to spare. Sometimes our best intentions to help would prove a hindrance and it seemed, most often, to happen to me.

Becoming bored very quickly with baby talk and female company, I had left the house. Mair, Mona and baby Tegwyn had come for a visit and after I had finished off any leftovers from afternoon tea I wandered around the yard looking for Mr Ladd and Benny, who were nowhere to be seen.

A speckled hen came out of the stable, clucking away, proclaiming to the world it had just laid a golden egg and this inspired me to collect the eggs for Megan. Imitating what she had done, I called to the chickens and threw them some grain but with hardly any response; the dogs didn't even get up. Determined to find more eggs than Megan, I disregarded the dipper and collected a bucket and entered the barn.

I quickly collected eggs from the nests that Megan had shown us, the only difference being that if a hen was on a nest I tried to frighten it off. If I failed to get a response a good poke with a sharp stick worked wonders. I climbed the ladder to the loft over the cowshed and a quick inspection by the light of the small window proved fruitless so I left the barn by the back door and entered the hay guard. Here I found some nests which contained smaller eggs and on one, a bantam refused to capitulate even when prodded with a stick. Finally with a screech of fury she flew up in my face, talons extended and wings flapping; we were eye to eye, and it was me who beat a hasty retreat. I continued my search in a more circumspect manner.

Against the back wall of the barn I checked out the old water wheel, frozen in time with rust. It had obviously supplied power for grinding wheat and cutting chaff. I couldn't resist climbing over it although the paddles were rotten or missing altogether. In the process, I disturbed a duck whose nest was secreted in the bottom of the wheel, and although the eggs were larger and of a greeny blue colour. I added another dozen to my rather mixed collection.

After checking the stable, my bucket was nearly full but I wanted to collect a real bucketful, right to the top. I stood and watched the hens going in and out of the derelict building and found myself in the open doorway. It smelt rotten, the manure having collected on the floor for many years. There were several hens sitting on makeshift nests around the walls and with a quick look around to see that I was unobserved, I was soon piling eggs into the bucket.

After I had removed most of the manure from my sandals I proudly carried the overflowing bucket of eggs into the house. Everyone was at the doorway saying goodbye to Mair and family but on my arrival there was a momentary silence as all eyes were drawn to the bucket. Rene had her mouth open but she made no sound. I just stood as they all started asking me questions and when things had quietened down Megan took me and the bucket outside.

Megan explained to me that over half of the eggs would be no good as they were in various stages of forming chicks and that eggs were collected from certain nests only, in the knowledge that they would be fresh. She also added that nests in the derelict building were never touched thus allowing the hens to hatch them so as to keep their number up, because in spite of the dogs, foxes were always a menace. But, the worst thing was having to admit that I had been disobedient in entering the unsafe building after having been warned to keep out of it. I was also aware that my behaviour had upset Rene which was the last thing I wanted to do. However, the pigs enjoyed their raw omelette that evening. I had, at least, made them happy!

The bellowing of a cow in the distance had become most irritating and kept us awake during the night. Now the beast had woken us early by performing directly underneath our window. I could also hear voices and jumped out of bed to see what was happening.

The cows were still in the cowshed and, with the exception of one, the heifers were standing patiently waiting to be returned to their pastures. It was the largest of the heifers that was making all the noise. Benny appeared with a halter and the heifer was tied securely to the front gate, then everyone sat down to breakfast. It transpired that the heifer was ready to go to the bull, which meant a six mile round trip by road to Tre-fach, the farm on the opposite side of the valley. Looking out of the window I could see the farm not much more than a mile away as the crow flies.

After breakfast Megan went to clean up the dairy, Mr Ladd took off with the milk churns and Benny went to the cowshed to let the cows out. Mrs Ladd stood by the heifer with Rene and me, telling us that she hoped the calf, when it arrived, was not a male. She then lifted the heifer's tail and pointed to an obvious discharge which, she said, confirmed it was wanting the bull, adding that it was a long way to walk for nothing and that the fee for the bull was not cheap either. I noticed that Rene had turned a deep shade of pink.

Benny returned and waited for the cows to head back down the lane before following them with the heifer and then he surprised us by asking Rene and me if we would like to join him.

The day was warming up again, and we had already traversed most of the route when we posted our letters with Mr and Mrs James, The Post, but I decided to go as it would be a good chance to talk to Benny. Much to my surprise, Rene decided to come too, and so we forsook the coolness of the dark interior of Dolrannog and set forth on a long hot journey, in the bright sunlight with a fractious cow.

Benny handed me the halter and all went well as we followed the rest of the cows before shutting them in their field. Then, with an open road in front of her, the heifer wanted to waste no more time and took off. Benny made a quick grab at the rope and with the three of us holding on, we managed to keep her from breaking into a run again. Nevertheless we were still travelling at a good speed, and any contestant in an Olympic marathon would have been hard pressed to pass us.

Although still sweating, our gasps for air had eased to steady breathing when the neighbouring dogs flew out of their gate barking savagely and frightening both the heifer and Rene and me, and off we went once more. A man came to the gate and called the dogs off and he and Benny entered into a shouting match which continued for the next half mile. Sadly, it was a contest which Benny had no chance of winning having so little breath left to spare.

We slowed down at the bottom of the mountain, passing Waun Uchaf with no chance of stopping to say hello. The old couple in the next cottage came out to see who was passing but by the time they reached their front gate all they saw was a cloud of dust.

The five barred wooden gate brought us all to a stop, and here we rested before going the last short distance to the road and Ty'n Rhos. On arriving at the shop Benny ducked in for some cigarettes, letting us go ahead as the heifer was now quieter and not pulling so hard on the rope. Benny was still in the shop when it disappeared from sight as we followed the road around a sharp bend where it fell steeply to the narrow stone bridge where I had already been soaked once. Then, the heifer broke into a run down the hill. Rene was helping too as we tried desperately to hold on to the rope. But we were not strong enough and Rene had to let go when it charged down the bank and headed into the river.

I was determined to keep dry on this trip and Rene yelled at me to take my sandals off and not get wet, as she ran across the bridge. By the time she reached the other side, the heifer and I were climbing out of the water and up the bank. Rene grabbed the rope just in time as my hands were red and getting sore, and although I managed to stay upright in the water I was still soaking wet and uncomfortable once again.

Having passed the turnoff to the Post Office, we were now in unfamiliar territory, but the heifer inexorably continued its journey with Rene and I tagging along behind. Ahead, the road forked but my sister and I had no part in the decision to keep left and we started to climb again.

Looking down into the valley we were confronted with a magnificent panorama which expanded as we climbed higher. Behind us the river flowed through farmlands before reaching the sea, and ahead of us it meandered along the floor of the valley, sometimes intertwined with the twisting road. The fields looked greener, and a chapel with tombstones scattered around it shone white in the sunlight. A few wisps of smoke proclaimed the occasional cottage. Directly opposite we could just make out Dolrannog. Built from the natural grey stone, it blended into the background of the mountain.

Benny managed to catch us up just as we reached the gate to Tre-fach, excusing himself by saying that Mrs James was a one for talking. I could have nominated a good number two. On noticing my disarray, Benny remarked that I should be sure to bring my bathing costume the next time I passed this way. This he thought very funny and Rene laughed too. I didn't think it was so funny. I was wet and uncomfortable with sore hands, aching arms and wet sandals that were about to disintegrate.

Nearly a dozen adults came out to greet us on our arrival and we were introduced to them all. After the dogs had quietened down and we had satisfied our thirst with mugs of fresh water, we were bombarded with the usual questions. Again, I acted dumb and retreated behind Rene. There were no young people in the extended family gathered around us and as I looked about me I couldn't help comparing Tre-fach with Dolrannog which looked so forlorn in the distance. Everything about Tre-fach was bigger, better and neater, no doubt due to the extra manpower available.

Eventually our effort was rewarded as Benny led the heifer to a small yard enclosed by a high stone wall. Rene and I were directed to sit on the top of the wall and not to move. Benny now had the heifer on a short rope and was circulating around the yard waiting for the bull to enter. I became excited as I waited for the bull to come charging out as in a Spanish bullring, and I thought Benny as brave as any matador, even though his regalia was somewhat different.

I was most disappointed when a big fat bull called

Ferdinand slowly ambled into the yard, also led by a man holding a rope which was attached to a ring in the bull's nose. After a cursory examination of the heifer and the audience, the bull's attention was drawn to the green tufts of grass growing along the base of the walls which it now started to chew. After some pushing and pulling the two men managed to get their charges circulating with Ferdinand following close behind the heifer. On the third attempt the bull managed to mount the heifer and just had time for a couple of quick thrusts before she appeared to go cross eyed, and her back legs collapsed under its weight.

The heifer stood in shock while the bull resumed his grazing and a general discussion broke out. Rene and I managed to deduce that Benny was not satisfied with the bull's performance, so amid much laughter and ribald comments the matadors had to incite their beasts to perform an encore. Finally everyone was happy. Ferdinand was taken back to his shed, some money was handed over and everyone shook hands as we made our way to the house for morning tea, leaving the now satisfied heifer standing quietly on her own.

The kitchen was much larger and lighter than Dolrannog's and we enjoyed the usual Welsh cakes and pancakes which were very good, but no better than the ones Mrs Ladd cooked on her big black stove.

I thought that the heifer would be eager to get back home so I took the rope in anticipation of being pulled up the hills. How wrong I was! The first part of our journey home was easy, being down hill as far as the little bridge, which was crossed without incident. From then on it was an uphill battle all the way.

66

On both sides of the road, growing in the dampness at the foot of the low stone wall, lush blades of grass survived the summer heat. At this moment, the heifer who had been placidly following, still in shock or dreaming happy dreams, decided she was hungry. This was not surprising as she had done more mooing than mowing over the past few days. I waited while the heifer grabbed a few mouthfuls of grass before trying to get her to move again, but to no avail. Benny came to my aid by giving her a few good slaps on the rump with his cap, causing us to shoot across to the other side of the road and this performance was repeated all the way to Ty'n Rhos. Here we stopped for a breather and a drink of water before taking the track up the mountain. Miss James came out to see us off, presenting Rene and me with a bull's eye each. Mine was brown with white stripes but I really preferred the black ones. She made us feel as if we were being presented with the crown jewels mentioning something about ration books, but on receiving a kick on the shins from Rene I remembered my manners and thanked her as we went on our way.

The man and his savage dogs were nowhere to be seen as we passed by and it was with a feeling of great relief that we opened the gate to let the heifer join the rest of the herd in their field.

Walking freely I was able to talk to Benny who was looking a little worried. He told Rene and me that this was the second time that the heifer had been to the bull, and if she could not produce a calf or milk she would be worthless. I asked Benny why Dolrannog didn't have its own bull, and after thinking for a while he answered my question saying it was for the same reason that they did not have a tractor. Seeing the puzzled look on my face he explained it was all to do with money. Then, letting his frustration flow he told us how different things would be when he was running the farm. Benny also told us he wanted to join the airforce adding that he would soon finish off the Germans if he could only fly a Spitfire, but like most young farmers he was manpowered. England was on short rations, though this was hard to believe with all the sheep and cattle grazing contentedly across the landscape.

Rene and I entered the farmhouse feeling hot and exhausted and even Benny looked a little tired. We went straight out the back and washed our hands and faces under the spout. The cool water soothed my sore feet which were now blistered. Flopping down on the couch next to Rene I was relieved not to have any more walking to do. I felt hungry and was looking forward to lunch.

However, Mrs Ladd was more concerned with a letter she was handing to Benny to read, and we both knew instantly by the look on their faces that it concerned us. We both became alarmed immediately thinking that something had happened to our parents and Rene became more agitated as Benny and Mrs Ladd continued to discuss the letter's contents in Welsh. Megan entered the kitchen and she too read the letter. She immediately calmed everyone down and told Rene and me that we had to report to the village hall in the morning.

My heart sank at the thought of another six mile walk. I told Mrs Ladd about my sore feet, which she duly treated with a thick red ointment which was used on the cows with sore udders and teats, and for any other purpose on the farm. Benny left the room laughing as he told me that not only would it make my blister disappear but if left on for too long my feet would disappear too. Obviously I was not going to be excused from the route march on medical grounds.

Chapter 5

IN THE VILLAGE

That night before bed, the big enamel bowl was taken off the table in the back room and placed on the floor. After filling it with hot water Mrs Ladd handed me a scrubbing brush and some red soap which had the same smell as the ointment and told me to scrub myself from top to toe. After having to rescrub my knees I was declared clean on the third inspection.

We sat around the breakfast table the next morning in silence and with little appetite, wondering what was going to happen to us and not looking forward to another long walk. I was wearing clean clothes and Benny had repaired my sandals for me and cleaned them with saddle soap. Rene had on a pretty summer dress with a matching ribbon holding her hair back from her face, which made her appear most vulnerable. We cheered up when Megan appeared also wearing a summer dress and shoes, instead of the usual clogs, and announced she was going to accompany us.

So once again we followed the lane which divided Dolrannog's land. On both sides low stone walls formed small fields, all sloping down from the mountain to the valley. A higher wall separated Dolrannog from the adjoining farm.

Where the fields ended abruptly the lane divided into two tracks leading across the open mountain side. The lower one dropped steeply past Waun Uchaf and joined the road at Ty'n Rhos; the higher track followed the contour of the mountain and joined the road where Mr Ladd delivered the milk to the truck. At this corner was the neglected looking farmhouse which Rene recognised from our arrival in the little Austin on the first night. Megan confirmed that we were walking over the same route and added that the name of the little building was New England which we thought most odd, but on being questioned further, Megan was unable to tell us if anyone still lived there.

The first half of our journey had passed most pleasantly with Megan trying to teach us Welsh songs, which resulted in bursts of laughter. The walking was quite painful at first but after a while our legs loosened up and the aches disappeared. The road continued to sweep around the mountainside gently dropping on its way to the village. Above us, on our left, the peaks always dominated the skyline as we passed the occasional cottage fronting the road. Below us, on our right, the land was less rocky and had been divided by stone walls into small green fields bearing testimony to the endeavours of the hard-working farmers.

We came to a substantial two storied house which Rene and I remembered from the ride in the Austin. In the daylight we could see the gardens were neglected and the green Rover sedan parked outside looked in need of a wash and polish. Megan told us it was the Vet's house and he

71

lived there on his own. His wife had died and his only child was away at college. Trying to overcome his sorrow and loneliness he had acquired a penchant for whisky and was now regarded as a menace on the road. His veterinary skills had in no way diminished though and he was still regarded as a fine vet and never failed to attend an emergency day or night, no matter where.

As we came closer to the village the cottages appeared more frequently, and at our approach each one produced a lady waiting to ambush us, either from the doorway or from the front gate. We were about to run the gauntlet of inquisitive ladies. At first the questions were directed in English at Rene and me, but when I noticed that Rene was peering straight ahead with lips firmly clamped together, I became suddenly deaf too. The questions were then directed in Welsh at Megan who, pleading lateness, managed to escort us through the bombardment almost without stopping.

Where the road divided to give alternative routes to the village, there stood a solid double storey house, behind which was a large shed also built from the same local grey stone with a tiled roof. There was no room for any garden and barely enough space to accommodate the big black limousine parked at the front of the house. A thick-set man wearing tweeds and a matching cap was fastidiously polishing the chrome-work with a bright yellow duster. At our approach he stopped and doffed his cap and wished us a good day. Megan told us that he bought all the rabbits caught in the area and sold them on to London. A sign proclaimed the house to be called 'Greystone' which we all thought to be most appropriate.

A little further on, the road dropped away almost perpendicularly, and seeing the hill in daylight we couldn't believe that any car, let alone an overloaded Austin 7, could climb such a gradient. With a sharp bend at the bottom and stone walls on either side, to have stalled or run backwards could indeed have been a disaster.

On rounding the bend we were able to inspect the ruins of the old castle in more detail than before. Situated higher up the slope, it could at first have been mistaken for another pile of rocks, but closer examination showed that the base of the square tower was still standing. Glass in a few of the narrow windows signified some sort of recent habitation. Megan was able to tell us that an old lady had once lived there as a recluse, and after she died it was years before anyone found her skeleton because a candle still shone every night in her window. The hairs on the back of my neck prickled as Megan continued, saying that the candle was still seen at times, as was the ghost of the old lady.

In stark contrast, on the other side of the road, the little church looked as neat as a new pin with the lawns surrounding the building looking as if they had been newly manicured. The graves were all kept in pristine fashion with fresh flowers in abundance. We walked through the grounds and read some of the inscriptions on the older headstones, but Megan was anxious to get us to the hall so we were kept moving.

Our little road skirted across the top of the village square then became a narrow street between two rows of terraced houses. This street was so narrow that the front doors opened directly on to the road without even a pavement to walk on. It was fortunate that cars were almost non existent as there was only room for one car at a time.

A blue lamp over one of the doorways proclaimed the local police station where a heavy old fashioned bike against the wall, indicated the flying squad.

After a few more houses, the narrow street merged with the main road, where on the opposite side two petrol pumps drew my attention to a garage where one of the buses was undergoing some work under the bonnet. A rusty sign advertised the fact that a taxi service was available.

Looking down the road we could see groups of people standing around outside the hall and as we joined them, memories of our last visit came flooding back. It was certainly a case of deja vu as the minister came to greet us, his Austin 7 parked near the wall. Once again, he was the only male present and we joined a group of ladies who were chatting away, making the most of the opportunity to turn the meeting into a social occasion. With the exception of a few boys playing ball, the children just stood next to their carers wondering what was about to unfold.

We slowly wended our way to the doorway at the side of the hall, where a lady was checking the number of people she admitted with those leaving. When it became our turn to enter, the hall was empty except for the few ladies sitting behind a couple of trestle tables.

Memories of our first night came flooding back and I looked at Rene hoping she was not about to burst into tears. We stood in front of the first table where the lady started to write down our answers to her questions on an official looking document. Once again, I let Rene do the talking. This lady was a social worker and she wanted to know if we were happy with our new family and also if they were happy with us. There was no problem there which Megan confirmed.

We were well behaved and didn't wet the beds. Apparently bed-wetting was causing problems with some of the evacuees in the village, though there were few complaints about behaviour. However, we did hear of two brothers who were to be moved from a widow's cottage. Apparently, she was a little eccentric and used an excessive amount of makeup, predominately white face powder and bright red lipstick. One day she returned home to find the boys made up as clowns and, not only had they used all of her makeup, they had also invaded the privacy of her bedroom.

More questions probed our contact with home, our basic needs of life and hygiene. We forgot to mention the lack of a toilet. Questions from another lady concerned our education but when Megan asked about when and where we would be starting school she was unable to give an answer. It was to be over six weeks before we started school and, under normal conditions, this would have been summer holiday time anyway.

The last lady we spoke to was a nurse who was very kind and caring towards us. I did not even mind her combing my hair to see if I had nits. She looked concerned when I stood on the scales to be weighed and even more so when she saw my feet, which were still red with scars from my blisters. She told me to wear shoes and socks for walking long distances and was alarmed to learn we would have to walk so far to school and asked how would we cope in winter. Megan told her that she had always walked to school. The nurse was still writing on our forms as we left, but she said that she hoped, for our sake, that the war was over before winter began.

We were glad to leave the hall and enjoy the sunshine again but I was disappointed to see that the minister's Austin had already left as I had been hoping for a ride home. This time Megan took us through the village which was squeezed between the sea and the foot of the mountain. We walked around the square where most of the shops and businesses were situated. On one corner, the Commercial Hotel stood tall being three storeys high and dominating the bank and the Post Office. The smell of freshly baked bread drew me towards the bakery where in the window a variety of bread, pies and cakes made my mouth water. Next door, was a shop selling ice-cream and Megan took us inside. There was no choice and no cones so we had one scoop of vanilla in a paper cup. Megan told us it was home-made from real cream, but to me, it tasted just like any other ice-cream. A rush of homesickness overcame me as I remembered the summer holidays at home when we would spend two weeks at the seaside as a family. As I spat some paper out of my mouth, I wondered if I would ever do that again. I noticed Rene had gone quiet too.

A large white house stood on a corner of the next crossroads and a highly polished brass plate on the door proclaimed that it was the doctor's house. Further down was the local school which looked more like a workhouse from a Dickens novel. The blacksmith's shop occupied the opposite corner to the doctor.

A narrow street crossed the main road and climbed steeply to the church. On both sides terraced houses faced each other, individualised by a different coloured front door and window frames. Stepped into the steep hill, like a giant's stairway, they appeared to have a most precarious footing as they all clung together as if waiting to fall like a pack of cards.

We carried on a little further, almost to the end of the village, and here, another narrow road crossed the main one. The low road led to the only bridge across the river but we took the high road which immediately started to rise to join our road home at Greystone.

We were soon hot and panting for breath and as we passed the cottages again the ladies appeared with their questions which again Rene and I ignored. We noticed that the green Rover hadn't moved from outside the vet's house. I put New England under scrutiny as I walked past. I couldn't see any smoke from the chimney and was about to concede that the place was empty when a curtain moved. I determined to find out more from Mrs Ladd.

The sweetness of the ice-cream made us thirsty and Megan soon found a trickle of cold water next to the wall and as we walked on she pointed out places where water could always be found. She also told us where to find wild strawberries and blackberries and where we would find nuts in the autumn.

We were all glad to enter the cool farmhouse away from the bright sunlight. My feet were sore and my legs ached. Rene was red in the face and even Megan had perspiration on her forehead as she went upstairs to change. Rene and I just flopped on the couch, thinking about the walks we had in front of us when we started school. As it transpired only two months were to elapse between our arrival at Dolrannog and starting school and it was during this time, though we didn't know it, that England was engaged in the Battle of Britain. News about the war was usually translated to us by Mrs Ladd who not wishing to cause us any more concern censored any depressing news. So when we received a letter from our mother saying that she and father were safe, we had no reason to disbelieve her. We had no idea that our father was on duty at the London Docks which were being bombed incessantly or that our mother was on night duty with the ambulance brigade. We were not told about the air raids on the Welsh docklands either and those took place only weeks after our arrival in Wales.

Chapter 6

MY BROTHER BENNY

The summer of 1940 was magnificent and Rene and I, although a little on the thin side, looked healthy under our newly acquired sun tan. Our ignorance of events shielded us from too much worry about the war and, as time passed by without the Germans invading, we felt confident of victory not too far away. In the meantime we adapted to the routine of the farm which revolved around milking times and we were determined to enjoy our freedom.

We learned a lot about farming and helped where we could, but we still had a lot of time on our hands. We seldom left the farm and mostly, we were content. We still suffered homesickness at times, especially when saying our prayers at night, when images of our real home and our parents would appear in our minds.

Life became more bearable for Rene as she and Mona became good friends, and she had someone her own age to talk to. Mona walked to Dolrannog though because Rene was still too nervous about the dogs down the lane to walk on her own to Waun Uchaf. There was no doubt that they enjoyed each other's company and there was no doubt either that they didn't want me tagging along and listening to their conversation. This allowed me time on my own and this later proved to be unwise.

It was on one such occasion that I was trying to amuse myself by making boats out of bark and goose feathers. I was trying to sail my fleet downstream across the farmyard and under the wall by the pigsty but I gave up after they had become stuck for the umpteenth time due to lack of water.

Behind the bottom wall of the farmyard was a row of trees, obviously planted as a windbreak and much used by the chickens to roost in. They reminded me of the poplars that grew alongside our back garden at home, having straight trunks and branches and plenty of leaves in the summer. I liked climbing although I was discouraged from doing so by my mother. Here was the perfect opportunity and I wondered if it would be possible to reach the top and swing from one tree to the next since they had been planted so close together.

After getting off the ground and onto the lowest branch, the rest of the ascent was as easy as climbing a ladder. I stopped before the top as the branches were getting thinner and the tree had started to sway under my weight. Looking at the next tree along I calculated that if I risked climbing a few feet higher I would be able to swing far enough over to reach it. The tree I had climbed was healthy and full of sap, and I didn't think it would snap, so I started swinging.

Just at this moment, Mrs Ladd came out of the house and I called out to her then watched in amusement as she looked about trying to find me. Finally, poking my head through the leaves, I told her where to look. I thought she was going to faint as she threw her apron over her head and screamed her way back into the house. I considered going down but decided to carry out my plan and descend by using the next tree anyway. But, while showing off to Mrs Ladd I had lost my concentration. Swinging across the gap was quite easy but as I grabbed the second tree I forgot to let go of the first and was now suspended between the two forming a perfect arch with a tree in each hand and my feet hanging in space thirty feet up in the air. Raw fear made my grip vice-like, but I realised I would not be able to hold on for long.

Fortunately Mr Ladd and Benny were inside having their afternoon cup of tea and Mrs Ladd, still screeching at the top of her voice and with her clogs clattering over the cobblestones now led them to me. Benny couldn't contain himself on seeing my predicament and, asking if the monkey would like a peanut or a banana, he burst into laughter. A quick rebuke from Mr Ladd sent Benny climbing to my aid. With his superior strength he stood under me and was able to pull the two trees together to allow me to let go of the first tree and follow him back to earth. Rene and Mona now appeared and I felt very small and foolish as I stood in the middle to be chided by all. My eyes were screwed tightly shut as I thanked Benny for saving me.

Of course my escapade was relived over the evening meal, and that was one occasion when I was glad when the time came to listen to the news.

Rene was still upset with me in the morning and again told me not to do any more stupid things. Not wishing to upset her further, I determined to make amends but after helping to feed the calves and taking the cows back to pasture after milking, I again found myself all alone. The three females were inside the house doing various chores where I was not wanted and did not want to be. Mr Ladd had left with the milk churns and I didn't know where Benny was.

My thoughts turned to my lucky escape of the previous day and I had an urge to return to the scene of the crime. Climbing the wall by the pigsty, I stood under the trees and wondered if I would have survived the fall. I shuddered as I felt the rocks that lay below the trees, hidden by the long grass. Hearing noises I cautiously raised my head above the wall and saw Benny approaching with the horse and cart, from the direction of Pen-rhiw, the other neighbouring farm.

Rene and I had been told to keep away from there, as the owner, who was old and a widower, lived in the village and only made sporadic visits to the farm. Benny kept an eye on a few dry cattle and the sheep up the mountain and was hoping that the property might become his one day.

Prince was a young cart horse, chestnut in colour with black mane and hairy fetlocks. He was not as big as a thoroughbred Shire, but was very strong nevertheless. He and Turpin made an ill matched pair when harnessed together. Prince was skittish with a wild look in his eye and it was usually only Benny who worked him.

The cart was heavy and cumbersome; its grey dry wood showing that no paint had ever touched its sides. The two high wheels were steel banded and made sharp screeching noises as they ran over the stony surface.

Now many people would say that Benny was a bit of a card and he did have a certain air about him. Only he could wear a cap at such a rakish angle. Only he could stand upright, legs apart, reins in hand as the cart jolted and jerked its way along the lane to the farmyard. In between bursts of song Benny would urge Prince on. Passing the hay guard they were about to pass through the open gateway between the cowshed and the wall and just where I happened to be. Since I was hidden behind the wall, my head was almost level with that of the horse and I decided to give Benny a surprise. So, letting loose my best Red Indian war cry, with arms waving, I leapt on top of the wall.

Benny certainly was surprised but less so than Prince who reared up on his hind legs, causing the cart to tilt and upsetting Benny's balance. The horse then lunged forward throwing Benny onto his bottom, as it took off at full gallop. Horse, cart and Benny with legs pedalling the air, careered across the farmyard. Geese, turkeys, ducks and hens with raucous cries of alarm tried desperately to escape from the pounding hooves and spinning wheels. With so many wings flapping and feathers flying, the yard looked as if it had been struck by a snow storm. The dogs arrived on the scene expecting to see a fox attack, but after completing three laps around the yard to no avail they stood looking at all the falling feathers with a puzzled expression on their faces.

Mrs Ladd, Rene and Megan came running from the house just in time to see a performance to make even Ben Hur envious, as Benny, with reins gripped tightly and at great speed, took the bend on one wheel before disappearing down the lane towards the village. I just prayed that Mr Ladd was not on his way home yet. Mrs Ladd covered her head with her apron and prayed for her only son before going back into the house followed by Megan and Rene. The dogs returned to their sleep under the porch and I decided to go for a walk towards the mountain. Looking down, I could see no sign of Benny, the horse or the cart.

Eventually I had to return to the house where everyone was seated around the lunch table and the silence was deafening. I cast a surreptitious glance at Benny, who, thankfully appeared to be in one piece, and sat down opposite my empty plate. I knew what it would feel like to be like to be a leper when even my sister moved a little away from me. Then all hell broke loose with everybody talking at once, and I didn't have to understand Welsh to know that Benny was calling for the death penalty or, at least, bed and no lunch for me!

As usual it was dear old Mr Ladd who, with his quiet voice, brought order to the table. With words of wisdom he made me see the foolishness of my actions, adding that the fact that Benny and the horse and cart had all survived was no thanks to me. I felt hot tears in my tightly screwed up eyes as I said I was sorry to Benny and ate my lunch in silence. I had been forgiven, but that night I wished I could have been in my own bed at home, where the only animal we had to worry about was Sally, our foxy. At least she knew how to play games. I made up my mind that I would never be a farmer, or a zoo keeper either. I felt very forlorn and isolated in my new country.

The following morning I walked out of the house determined to keep out of trouble. I declined Mr Ladd's offer to accompany him on the milk run, remembering the aches and pains and bruised bottom I had received on my first trip. I felt even more guilty when Mrs Ladd told me at breakfast that Benny was stiff and sore after the incident and that he had required minor surgery with a darning needle to remove splinters from some very funny places.

I found Benny by the woodpile sharpening a crosscut saw with a file. There was only one dead branch left to cut. The wood pile was getting low and Benny said he was waiting on Mr Ladd's return to get some more. He also told me there was a busy time ahead for the farm and everything had to be ready for making hay and the harvest.

Finishing with the file, Benny told me to work one end of the saw and we set about cutting the branch into logs. I was soon hot and tired. I couldn't get the saw to cut at all but Benny kept urging me on, saying how weak I was. When Benny could no longer contain himself and had burst into laughter, I realised that he had tricked me by not working his end at all but only pretended to! I gave a wry smile acknowledging that he had evened the score, but he still hadn't finished with me. We had quickly sawn up the branch after Benny had shown me the correct technique and pulled his weight as well, and now the logs had to be split and stacked against the wall of the house.

I turned the handle of the wet stone while Benny put an edge on the axe, which he then honed and finally, after shaving a few hairs off his arm, declared it sharp enough. Pieces of wood went flying as Benny split the logs into pieces, more quickly than I could stack them. He stopped to wait for me to catch up and then pointing to the last five logs by the chopping block, he challenged me to split them in under one minute.

Reminding me of the number of fingers and toes I had

and urging me to keep my feet clear, Benny showed me how to swing the axe. It was much heavier than I had anticipated but I had no trouble in splitting the first log as Benny counted off four seconds. I quickly calculated that it would take me less than half a minute to complete the task when Benny suggested we had a bet for sixpence. I couldn't agree quickly enough, and didn't even consider the fact that I didn't own a halfpenny, I was so confident.

The first four logs were split in under thirty seconds and I was already making plans to spend my winnings as Benny placed the last log on the chopping block. I did notice it was a little different in shape, having come from the thick end of the branch, but I was not prepared for the axe glancing off it and sinking into the chopping block. Benny kept on counting and I only had ten seconds left when I let go another mighty swing and this time the axe rang true and sank into the piece of wood, but without splitting it. In fact, it had gripped the axe so tightly that I still hadn't got it free after five minutes. Again, Benny had me red of face and out of breath while all he could do was laugh. We hadn't noticed that Mr Ladd had returned and was watching us. Handing the reins to Benny, he looked at the axe still embedded in the log and showed me how the grain ran in all directions. He then told me that only a special tool called a log splitter could chop through a piece of wood like that. Speaking in English, he told Benny that he had acted in a very stupid manner and had put me in danger by letting me use such a heavy axe. Benny's reply was in Welsh, but turning to me he said he would be pleased if I would go with him to fetch more wood, quietly adding that he had a surprise for me too.

Mr Ladd went into the house and I helped Benny free Turpin from the cart after unloading the empty churns. Usually, after the milk run Turpin was free to graze but this morning the harness was left on and a light chain was allowed to drag behind. The horse became fractious as I led him past his field and down the lane. Benny came behind with the axe and thumped Turpin with the handle thus ending his nonsense. We followed a wall along two fields undoing a makeshift gate on the way and arrived at the top of the valley. The ground fell away steeply here. It was damp underfoot and slippery with wet moss growing on rocks. It smelt of mould and the sides of the valley were covered in small trees which kept us in shade. We carefully picked our way down avoiding prickly undergrowth and looking out for a suitable dead tree to cut down. We reached the bottom without mishap where we were halted by a stout fence. We left Turpin to nibble at the grass along the fence line with the chain stopping him from going too far away, and climbed over. Benny took a good look around before stepping into the bright sunlight. We were now in a different world.

The cold dampness of the shade had caused goose-bumps to rise on me. These now quickly disappeared as the heat from the sun and the humidity hit me as if someone had opened an oven door; the brightness made me squint. It was still, with not the slightest breeze, and I watched a hawk high in the sky hovering patiently, waiting for something to move. The floor of the valley varied in width as it curved towards the coast, being a mile or so at its widest point and sometime only half that. It was totally flat with the narrow road and the river twisting and turning together, changing sides when they came to a narrow stone bridge. Smoke rising from a chimney indicated the occasional farm or cottage.

I was behind Benny as we walked in lush green grass along a hedgerow towards the river. As we neared the bank he told me to be very quiet because we were going to catch some fish. I was immediately on guard expecting another trick from Benny. I knew enough about fishing to realise that some bait was required, and also some hooks and lines. We had absolutely nothing.

Warily I watched from a distance as Benny rolled up his sleeve and crept along the edge of the bank looking for something in the water. Finding the right spot he lay down and slowly extended his bare arm into the water. Nothing happened for a while and I was starting to get bored when, with hardly a splash, Benny flicked a fish out of the water and onto the bank in my direction. I was about to jump up and yell out in excitement but again Benny motioned for me to keep quiet as he moved a little further along the bank. I tip-toed to where the fish was going through its death throes causing the sun to reflect the vivid colours of its scales. It was not the biggest of fish being less than twelve inches long; I couldn't help feeling sorry for it as its spasms finally ceased.

It took Benny nearly an hour to catch a dozen trout and I wasted twenty minutes trying to copy him without even seeing or feeling a fish. After the fish were threaded through their gills onto a green stick which I was allowed to carry, we made our way back along the hedgerow to Turpin. I couldn't help noticing that Benny kept looking around a lot, but he avoided my questions, and instead told me of the technique he had used to catch the fish.

First he would look for a bubble coming from the shade of the river bank. He would then quietly slip his hand into the water and, moving very slowly, he would gently stroke the fish under its stomach. This would mesmerise the fish which was then swiftly thrown onto the bank. Very few people developed the art of 'tickling' fish.

We then climbed the steep slippery slope of the valley to where Benny had spotted a suitable tree. With a few deft strokes of the axe he soon had the tree secured by the chain and Turpin was straining every muscle as we staggered to the top. The branches of the dead tree tangled with the undergrowth at times, bringing Turpin to a halt, and Benny had to chop a way through. We eventually made it to the top, hot and out of breath.

Eventually, the tree was dragged to the woodpile and Turpin was free to graze. In great excitement, I ran to the house to show Mrs Ladd our catch, expecting a warm welcome as I handed her the fish. I was disappointed when she took them with a frown. I thought perhaps that she didn't like fish, but this was not the case, as she ate it with the rest of us. There was a general discussion amongst the family as they ate the fish and I could tell by the tone of their voices that something was wrong. However, Benny seemed quite unperturbed as he left the table, pointing to the empty plates and laughing.

Megan told Rene and me later that Benny and I had been fishing on the property of the farm with the barking dogs and had, therefore, been trespassing. Benny and I were poachers, but that was not our last feed of trout!

Chapter 7

LIFE WITH THE ANIMALS

I asked Benny why the horses had English names and he told me that they already had their names when Dolrannog bought them and in Prince's case this was not so long ago. Benny was not happy with Prince who, except when pulling the heavy plough with Turpin, was always skittish and difficult to control. With the harvest about to be gathered, the last thing they needed was a runaway horse, and Mr Ladd agreed with Benny that Prince should be castrated. In answer to my question Benny took great delight in explaining the details of castration and ended by saying that I too would benefit from the same operation. I did not really understand what it was all about but I did notice that Rene was blushing.

A few mornings later two men arrived at Dolrannog to help perform the grisly deed. All the gates were shut after Benny had led Prince to the front of the house where the ground was relatively flat and smooth. Prince was tied to the front gate while Benny honed the cut-throat razor on a leather strop; Mr Ladd arrived with some short coils of rope. Becoming aware of the attention he was receiving and of the two strange men standing close by, Prince flattened his ears and with both eyes rolling decided to make a bolt for it, but to no avail.

Rene and I had a good view from behind the wall near the pig sties where we had been sent. We had been warned to keep still and quiet. It became obvious that the men knew exactly what they were doing as, in spite of Prince's struggle, they soon had him secured in a web of rope. I heard Rene gasp as the final coup de grace came and the men pushed the horse over, causing him to land on his side with a thud. Prince was now making peculiar noises and frothing at the mouth; his whole body was trembling as he gasped for breath. The men were also gasping for breath after their exertions and paused for a moment before Benny performed the final act.

Like a scene from the Coliseum in Rome the four men sat on the fallen horse, with Benny at the rear holding the razor high in the air like a gladiator. Swiftly he made the final cuts before raising his hand which contained two round objects covered in blood. These he threw to the waiting dogs who swallowed them whole in one second.

The men moved quickly to untie the ropes and take cover behind the front gate before the horse could rise. Prince struggled to his feet standing stiff legged at first; he was shaking and splashed with foam and blood. I am sure he looked at me before taking off at full gallop straight towards me. I thought he was going to jump the wall but he veered off at the last moment. After doing a few laps of the farmyard he stood with bowed head in one corner snorting and breathing heavily. He still hadn't moved when we came back outside after lunch. I hadn't felt very hungry because I couldn't help feeling guilty and thinking that by my stupid behaviour I had caused Prince to suffer.

Prince was back in harness a few days later, apparently fully recovered, at least physically. Benny led a subdued Prince, with a heavy hay cart trundling behind, across the farmyard in front of the house. Wishing to enter the yard Benny called me to hold the horse, telling me to hold tight to the ring on the bit. I was on my own. I had never been this close to a cart horse. Saliva was trickling down my hand as Prince chomped on the bit, showing his huge yellow teeth. Changing my grip I wiped my hand along his neck and was surprised by how soft and silky it felt. Prince's head was slightly above mine and I could feel his hot breath on my face as I looked up at him. His eyes were dark brown with long lashes which gave him a soft expression and I thought he looked like a gentle giant. Then he took one step forward and his heavy steel-shod hoof landed on my foot. I was only wearing my worn out sandals and I stood in fear as I waited for Prince to put all his weight down on me. We stood frozen together for a few seconds and I am sure that it was a look of amusement that I saw in his eye! Then, plucking up courage and pushing on the bit, I ordered Prince to back up. Obediently and with great care, he removed his giant hoof from my foot without transferring any of his great weight onto me.

I was stroking Prince on the velvety part of his nose when Benny came out of the house and I felt proud as I told him that Prince had behaved well and given me no trouble at all. But, I had strong reservations when Benny, on climbing onto the cart, told me he would make a farmer out of me yet. Farming was not on my list of possible careers!

We had soon became aware that life on a farm was tough. The people seemed to work very hard for very little reward and even the animals were treated in a seemingly unfeeling, if not cruel way. The screams of the rabbits as they were caught in Benny's traps kept us awake at night, the steel jaws holding them fast by their shattered legs till they were put out of their misery in the morning.

One morning I was up early and accompanied Benny as he went to empty his traps and reset them. Although I admired his skill as he explained to me the art of setting and concealing a trap, my sympathies were wholly with the rabbit. Its eyes reflected the pain and the fear it was suffering before Benny released it from the trap and quickly broke its neck, and then gutted it with one slash of his knife; the guts would fall to the ground.

These traps also took their toll on the wildlife. On this particular morning, a magnificent eagle was caught by its talons and was desperately trying to fly away but each time, the short chain brought it crashing back to earth. It couldn't have been in the trap for long as it was still full of fight and Benny was not able to get close to it, so finding a stout stick he caved its skull in – much to my horror. Benny's only comment was that it would not attack any more lambs.

Domestic animals also sometimes fell foul of these traps. These were not regularly fed, because it was believed that if hungry, the cats and dogs could always catch a rabbit. So it was not uncommon to see a dog limping around with a sore foot or to find a cat in the trap; indeed it was surprising it did not happen more often. It was also surprising that through some instinct, the cats and dogs never attacked the farm animals; baby ducks and chickens would have made an easy meal. I hated those traps and never went trapping with Benny again.

Later, I learned that there were also other ways to catch a rabbit which created some excitement unless you happened to be the rabbit. Benny and I were walking through the top fields on our way up the mountain to check on some sheep. Being the highest, these fields were also the least arable, containing more rocks than the lower pastures and also clumps of prickly gorse. It was a warm afternoon and the dogs were quite happy to follow behind. They ignored the rabbits that ran away at our approach, some to their holes in the dry stone walls and others content to hide in the prickly gorse bushes.

Benny showed me how the rabbits made little tunnels in the bushes with one end for entering and one for leaving. He also seemed to know which bushes were occupied by a rabbit. Benny was wearing his overalls and heavy boots with steel heel and toe caps. Telling me to watch, he called the dogs to attention and then with a run and a jump he landed in the middle of a small gorse bush. In a flash he was on the ground with his arm up to the shoulder in the exit tunnel. When he withdrew it, he was holding a very startled rabbit.

The dogs were now awake and barking excitedly, sending rabbits running helter skelter for cover. Benny was laughing as he jumped on several more bushes, sometimes without result and sometimes with the rabbit bolting out of its tunnel to be chased by the dogs. As the dogs became more hot and tired, more rabbits succeeded in escaping.

With a flick of his pocket knife Benny slashed the guts

out of the biggest rabbits promptly giving the dogs something to squabble over. I was given the task of carrying the rabbits. I was sick of the smell of them by the time we returned home followed by an ever increasing swarm of flies. From then on, rabbits quickly slipped down the list of my favourite foods.

Another method of reducing the rabbit population took place at dusk, usually in a field with a young crop of tender shoots which the rabbits found irresistible. An inspection of such a paddock would be made in daylight and, with shovels, the men would walk around the stone walls filling up the majority of the rabbit holes, leaving a few of the most used untouched. They then made a mental note of their position. At dusk the men would return and a lighted storm lamp would be placed on a high spot in the middle of the field. As it became dark the rabbits were attracted from their burrows to the light. The men would then very quickly walk around the stone walls placing nets over the open holes in the burrows. When this task was completed, a signal was given and the dogs were let loose and guns fired in the air, causing the rabbits to flee to their holes only to be entangled in the nets. They were then easily dealt with causing minimal damage to the crop. This method, called 'lamping', was not used very often during the war as the blackout regulations prohibited naked lights.

Benny also used ferrets to drive the rabbits out of their burrows into the nets, but the ferrets always seemed to escape, and Mr Ladd refused to let Benny keep any more because they not only attacked rabbits but also poultry.

When the man from Greystone arrived in his small truck to buy the rabbits Benny always tried to get a better price from him, and lengthy discussions would take place inside the barn. If Benny was successful in obtaining a higher price he could not contain himself till he was able to let Emrys know.

For most of the year the pigs wandered at will. The two pig sties built into the farm yard wall, were only used when a sow was about to give birth, to fatten a couple of pigs for market or to ring the young porkers. We learned that pigs can do a lot of damage to crops and paddocks when they dig the ground up with their grizzly snouts. To prevent this they had a ring put in their nose though it actually looked more like a spike. The pigs were driven into a sty where a wrestling match took place with a couple of men. One man tried to hold the pig while the other tried to hammer the spike through the pig's nose. The screams of the pigs could be heard over on the other side of the valley, as could the men's curses. By the end of the operation there was little difference in smell between the pigs and the men!

When the time came for a sow to give birth she would be shut in the sty where rails had been fixed against the inside walls. These were to keep the sow from crushing her babies when lying down. Clean straw would be scattered on the floor. If the sow had an extra large litter, the weakest would often die from lack of milk. Again, the survival of the fittest. Another rather dangerous practice was pulling out the milk teeth of the piglets. This was done to protect the sow's teats so she would not stop feeding them. Of course, the mother sow became most upset when the men separated her from her piglets, and more so when the piglets complained loudly as their teeth were removed with pliers. But it was a lovely sight when the mother and her piglets were let out of the sty. The mother, with her beady eyes on the world, would lead a dozen or more little pink piglets, who followed behind like a string of pork sausages.

One thing that caused Rene and me much frustration and misery was the Welsh language. It sounded so strange to our ears and apart from some basic phrases, we never did learn to speak it. Benny went to a lot of trouble giving me private coaching, which Mr Ladd promptly forbade when I innocently called Mrs Ladd a silly old cow! Benny had assured me it meant a very kind lady.

Welsh was the everyday language. English may have been heard in the village during the summer when a few holidaymakers appeared briefly, but in the valley and on the mountain no other language was spoken. A couple of bus loads of evacuees were not about to change hundreds of years of custom and tradition and indeed why should they?

Our Welsh family did not intend to make Rene and I feel ignored. Indeed, everyone went out of their way to make us feel welcome but it was just perfectly natural for them to speak in their native tongue.

During the day it was not too disconcerting as I would spend time with Mr Ladd or Benny, helping or hindering. Rene would spend time with Megan or Mona and on a one to one basis the language was always English. In a group situation, however, such as mealtimes or evenings around the fire, the conversation was in Welsh. This precluded Rene and me from being part of the social group.

We had been properly brought up and taught good manners so we remained silent while adults were talking, which meant we sat in silence for most of the evening. What was particularly frustrating was when we were asked a question in English and our reply was discussed in Welsh.

For the best part of the evening Rene and I would just sit and look at each other, not understanding what was being said around us. The light of the one oil lamp was too dim to read or write by and we had no games to amuse ourselves with. This gave us too much time to think and, feeling isolated both geographically and mentally, our thoughts would naturally turn to home. We missed the feeling of belonging to a family, even though our new family was very concerned for our welfare and showed us every kindness. Fortunately, we were usually exhausted at the end of the day and going to bed early was not a hardship. We were to find that our problems would increase as summer changed to winter and the nights grew longer and days shorter. Although we never learned to speak much Welsh, we did in time come to understand most of a conversation.

After our arrival, Dolrannog received many visitors from neighbouring farms all wanting to see the Ladd's evacuees. Their curiosity was soon satisfied but there was one persistent visitor and he came to see Megan, not us!

Wynfred would arrive in his navy blue Morris 8 sedan which, though old, was in pristine condition. Benny couldn't take his eyes off it, and when Wynfred and Megan disappeared up the mountain for their evening stroll he would sit in the driver's seat and fiddle with the controls. It took all of Mr Ladd's authority to keep Benny from taking it for a drive.

Mrs Ladd relished telling us of Megan's great

achievement at finding the perfect partner. In her eyes, Wynfred was a wealthy man who owned a large farm at the other end of the valley and milked thirty cows by machine. He lived alone in a large house which had running water and electric light. Also, Wynfred looked nothing like a farmer. He was not as tall as Megan and was of slight build. He wore glasses and his receding hair made him look older than he really was. Wynfred was always spotlessly turned out. He wore a suit or jacket, a cap on his head and even managed to keep his shoes clean and shining. He was a strict teetotaller, a non smoker and highly respected as an elder of his chapel. In fact, his smart appearance made one think that he had just come from chapel. Even though we realised that he would take Megan from us one day, we couldn't help but like Wynfred. On his arrival he would always stop and talk to us. He cheered us up by saying that the war would soon be over and that we would be back in our own home before long. In the meantime, he urged us to enjoy our time with the Ladd family in Wales. One thing we liked in particular was that he didn't ask us a lot of questions.

Another person who appeared quite regularly on the scene was Mr Jenkins who owned Pen-rhiw, the next farm along from Dolrannog. He was the old man who did not live on the farm but in the village, driving up a couple of times a week in his horse and trap. There was only one way to Pen-rhiw and that was through Dolrannog's yard, the lane then continued past the cow shed and hay guard to the front gate of Pen-rhiw. Benny would complain about Mr Jenkins not farming properly, and apart from a few dry cattle the only other animals were his sheep which were left up on the mountain most of the time. Rene and I had inspected Pen-rhiw through the gate, and the house and the buildings looked very solid and in excellent repair, which was more than could be said about Dolrannog. Mr Jenkins could not speak English but he would smile and give us a wave as he passed through. He did not stop and talk to anybody else either, I thought he seemed lonely.

Rene and I were waiting for the cows to enter the field after morning milking and they were still blocking the lane when Mr Jenkins arrived on his way to Pen-rhiw. He waited patiently, watching us as we finally shut the gate behind the last cow, before beckoning us into the trap with him. I jumped at the chance but Rene was more hesitant, for he was a strange looking person. He looked rather like a run down squire in his unpolished leather boots and leggings, into which he had stuffed his much-stained corduroy trousers. The neckband of his collarless flannel shirt matched the colour of his jacket which was brown with green patches of mould and the same colour as his bowler hat. This had lost all shape, and was unlikely to have been worn by any self-respecting scarecrow. Wispy white hair straggled down from under the bowler's undulating brim and white whiskers and bushy white eyebrows gave his face a rather monkey-like appearance. Nicotine stains on his chin confirmed that it was a plug of tobacco that he was chewing. As I took in all these details I became aware that he was watching me intently with piercing blue eyes.

The trap must have been as old as Mr Jenkins. Two steps helped entry by the back door. The high wheels were fitted with narrow solid rubber tyres, and the wooden spokes were finely carved. Rusty springs softened the ride. I quickly jumped in and Rene followed more slowly. Mr Jenkins sat on the front seat and we sat on the side seats facing each other. The seat cushions were padded with horse hair which was escaping from the seams. A brass handrail was fixed all the way round the trap and a brass driving lamp was attached to each side. All the brass had turned green.

Both Mr Jenkins and his trap looked as if they had seen better days, but the horse was a magnificent specimen. It was pure white and its coat shone like silk in the sunlight. It was not breathing heavily or showing any signs of tiredness even though it had just pulled Mr Jenkins uphill all the way from the village.

After checking that we had shut the door properly Mr Jenkins picked up the reins, and the horse immediately broke into a trot. Mr Jenkins turned to look at us. He failed to see Rene's knuckles showing white as she gripped the brass handrail, but he did notice my grin of approval and gave the horse a flick on the rump with the whip. This had the same effect as pushing down on the accelerator of a sports car and the horse took off in full flight, tail streaming and ears flattened. It was an exhilarating experience with the high wheels spinning and the springs working overtime to smooth out the bumps. The hedgerows were flying by us as the pounding hooves of the horse sent up small clouds of dust.

In no time we were approaching the sharp bend in the lane just before entering Dolrannog's yard Mr Jenkins pulled on the reins to slow the horse down, not wanting to meet anyone head on at that speed, but the horse had other ideas. It was enjoying the run home and with the bit between its teeth there was no stopping it. Gripping the brass rail with both hands, mouth open and hair flying, Rene looked ahead in horror as we approached the sharp bend and even I could feel the hairs on the back of my head starting to prickle. Leaning over at an incredible angle the horse charged around the bend while we all hung on for dear life. Luckily for us nothing was coming in the opposite direction. We charged through Dolrannog's farmyard cutting a swathe through the chickens and ducks which, unfortunately, Mrs Ladd had decided to give some scraps to. She had a close view of the performance, in fact too close a view. She decided to call on her saviour, drop the bowl of scraps and join the fowls in a hasty retreat.

We passed quickly from sight as the horse took us past the cowshed and along the last stretch of lane before stopping at Pen-rhiw's front gate which was thankfully shut. Thanking Mr Jenkins for the ride we shakily made our way back to Dolrannog where we found Mrs Ladd recounting the drama to Mr Ladd in an almost hysterical way. They were relieved to have us back safely and promptly forbade us from having any other contact with Mr Jenkins or his fancy horse and trap. This order, as it turned out, was unnecessary as we never saw Mr Jenkins again. He died of a heart attack shortly after that and Pen-rhiw was put up for sale.

Chapter 8

BREAD, BUTTER AND WHINBERRIES

As we became more accustomed to our environment we found ourselves drawn more and more into the daily and at times, stifling routine of the farm. Rain, hail or shine, twice a day and every day the cows had to be milked.

Indeed it soon became apparent that the farm's very existence depended on the milk being ready in the churns in time for delivery to the milk truck. The milk cheque was waited for with trepidation in case any milk had been rejected. This could happen in the summer even though Megan cooled the milk twice. The heat of the sun and the shaking up of the churns on their journey to the factory could make the milk turn sour. Megan also told us that during a long winter, feed could be in short supply, and this could cause the butter fat content of the milk to fall below the acceptable level.

Although other cash crops were grown, these were of small amounts because of the lack of arable land. Also these crops were at the mercy of the elements; frost could devastate a potato crop and rain could ruin a harvest.

Although everybody helped each other during busy times we learned that each member of the family had his own area of responsibility.

Mr Ladd milked twice a day and took the churns to meet the truck. On Fridays he would wear a clean shirt and his second best jacket and after delivering the churns he would proceed to the village. Here he would leave the accumulator belonging to the wireless at the garage to be re-charged while he carried out other errands. The shopping would be minimal because apart from tea, sugar, salt and tobacco for the men, the farm was self sufficient.

Mrs Ladd's duties more or less confined her to the house, where she was always busy cooking or washing or cleaning. She would only milk in an emergency, and being a very large woman I'm sure she found it very uncomfortable sitting on a small three legged milking stool.

Megan milked twice a day with Mr Ladd and filtered and cooled the milk into the churns. She also made the butter and helped Mrs Ladd in the house.

Benny also milked twice a day unless he was working the horses, ploughing or harvesting. He did all the heavy work around the farm.

As our stay became extended we became more aware of the seasonal changes which produced different challenges and it was the elements not the war that had the greatest influence on our lives. As the magnificent summer of 1940 reached out to autumn there were no bad omens to warn us of things to come.

During our first weeks at Dolrannog we had felt rather shy and awkward and it was Megan who had gone out of her way to reassure us. With her bright and breezy manner she was able to lift our spirits, and she seemed to understand our terrible homesickness. She had become our big sister.

Rene and I were wondering what to do. We had just finished lunch with the family. It was hot outside but the men left the room to return to their jobs. As we stood to leave Megan asked us if we would like to help her make butter and of course we were delighted to have something to do.

We entered the back room where the butter churn stood on its trestle in the corner between the back door to the pantry which I had so far been unable to raid, so still had a clear conscience on that score. We had been shown a separator when visiting Mair at Waun Uchaf, and I had been allowed to turn the handle. This machine separated the milk and cream most efficiently leaving behind only butter milk. Megan told us that Dolrannog didn't own one. Instead, a little cream was taken from each day's milking and stored in the pantry until there was enough to churn. The pantry was always cold and Megan told us it even froze in the winter. The back roof of the house had been extended almost to the ground and had white plaster daubed over the black slate tiles for coolness. The back of the house had also been set into the slope of the mountain. This helped as an insulator.

The three of us dragged the heavy wooden butter churn into the middle of the room and a wooden tub was placed underneath. The churn was locked into position with the opening at the top. I was sent out to the back for some water which was then poured into the churn. Megan closed the hatch and, releasing the lock, gave it several quick spins. We could hear the water splashing around inside as it bounced over the wooden slats. On releasing the hatch, the water was allowed to fall into the tub which

I emptied outside. Then Megan put her nose into the churn and gave a few good sniffs explaining that there could not be the slightest smell of sourness if it was to make fresh-tasting butter. So Rene and I had a good sniff too, just to make sure!

After checking that the churn was secure we then entered the pantry to fetch the cream. This had been carefully skimmed, day by day, little by little, from the milk churns before they left the farm still containing the requisite amount of cream.

Rene and I gingerly carried the bowls of cream to the dairy for Megan who carefully emptied them into the churn. When we had finished, the churn was about a third full which Megan assured us was just the right level.

We then all took turns on the handle and of course I had to turn it more quickly than anyone else until Megan pointed out that the centrifugal force I was creating stopped the cream from leaving the sides of the churn and that never would I make butter all that speed.

Another little trick was the 'sighing' or 'breathing'.

Apparently after the churn had been turned for about five minutes, gas would build up. This was released by removing a cork-like bung, and the escaping gas would sound like a sigh. When the sigh ceased the butter was ready to form. This could be heard as a thump as the butter solids fell from the top to the bottom of the rotating churn.

It was now time to drain off the buttermilk and this was set aside for drinking, cooking or adding to the pigs' or calves' feed. The churn now had cold water added to it, to wash the butter as it turned slowly. This was repeated several times until the water came out crystal clear and then, finally, the butter was allowed to leave the churn. The result was rather a disappointment to us for it came out as a white, wet, soggy mess. It was placed on a large wooden board and Megan set about it with her corrugated wooden paddles, sending sprays of water all over the table. Rene and I both had a go but we were unable to control the slippery mess. It didn't take long for Megan to tame the beast and with the addition of salt she soon had it knocked into blocks of the farm butter we enjoyed so much.

Of course everything had to be thoroughly rinsed and left ready for next time and I was kept busy bringing in or emptying copious quantities of cold water, a good proportion of which somehow finished up all over me. At least I was less aware of the heat of the sun.

Most of the time we would be outdoors in the bright sunshine. Mona would sometimes join us and we would make up games or explore the countryside. On one occasion we were allowed to climb to the top of the mountain equipped with paper bags in case there were whinberries ripe for picking.

The whinberry was a small black berry that grew in the summer on a low scrubby bush. It appeared to grow from the grey rocks and only near the top of the mountain. The flesh was purple and stained anything it touched such as fingers and lips, but it also made a very tasty filling for Mrs Ladd's fruit pies.

The climb up the mountain was quite gentle at first as we just followed the sheep trails across the open ground. Mrs Ladd had warned us to keep away from the wild horses as the stallions became very aggressive at certain times of the year. Mona didn't seem at all apprehensive and in any case we didn't see any, though I did notice that Rene was keeping a good lookout.

The trails wandered in every direction between the big rocks and the prickly gorse bushes. Bracken was the only other plant to flourish, its shiny green fronds still softening the slopes at this time of the year before turning to brown in the winter.

Even though it was mid-summer there were still patches of damp moss growing at the base of the rocks and we took care not to step on it as it was very slippery. In places there was water trickling down the mountain face to join and form ever faster flowing streams. As we neared the summit we could smell the sea and a fresh cooling breeze hit us. We were now climbing over huge grey rocks that some giant upheaval centuries ago had forced up from the bowels of the earth and, of course, I was determined to be the first to the top.

Mona and Rene were following me on an ill defined path that twisted and turned its way to the top. This route was used by the locals and was neither too arduous or dangerous. In spite of warnings from Mona and threats from my sister I opted for a more direct approach. At first I climbed quickly, jumping from rock to rock, but as I approached the summit the rocks became larger leaving gaping holes in between. A fall into one of those holes would certainly cause injury, if not death. I suddenly came up against an extra large rock which completely blocked my way and on looking down a deep dark hole next to it, I froze. It was hard to keep my balance in the gusty wind, and I had to sink to my hands and knees. It was in this manner that I managed to climb back down to the girls, unsuccessfully trying to hide my fright and keep my hands from shaking. Feeling rather stupid by now, I was quite content to follow them to the summit which we reached without further incident.

Mona warned us to hang on tightly before poking our heads over the top which, we did. The force of the wind coming from the ocean would certainly have blown us over had we not done so. Screwing up our eyes against the cold blast, we were able to see the most wonderful panorama unfold below us. Little farms nestled amid neatly walled fields and we could see the little white cottages that lined the road into the village.

The village straggled down to the ocean, and because the tide was in, the river filled the estuary which formed a magnificent bay. At each end there protruded a striking headland. White spray tried to climb the cliffs as the waves crashed on the rocks below. Somewhere, the blue sea and the blue sky merged, a slight haze obscuring the precise line of the horizon and the distant coast of Ireland.

With our eyes watering from the cold we ducked down out of the wind and behind us the panorama continued. The hills and dales stretched away to the horizon and we could see where the first sweep of the valley began from where the river emerged to wend its way seaward. More farms and cottages were sprinkled across the landscape and Mona pointed out to us some familiar landmarks like the chapel and the tiny post office. Dolrannog was hidden from view but Tre-fach stood out boldly on the opposite side of the valley.

It was a countryside that we were now becoming a part of, a countryside of extremes which as yet we had not experienced. It was to become a place we hated at times and a place we eventually loved but we had not yet come to understand it. Eventually, it became to us the most beautiful place in the world, but we had not yet been tested by the harsh winter climate.

After satiating ourselves with the views we set about looking for whinberries. As we dropped lower down among the rocks, the temperature soon rose again and the wind abated to a pleasant breeze. The berries were not abundant and after scrambling over the rocks for about an hour our paper bags were only half full but enough, Mona said, for Mrs Ladd to make a few pies with.

Our fingers were stained purple from the juice, our lips were also purple from having to sample some just to make sure they were ripe. We had about an hour's walk back to the farm and as we reached the lower slopes it became quite warm again. We refreshed ourselves at the small streams, noticing that the water made no difference to the colour of our lips or fingers; the juice made a very good dye.

The paper bags became rather soggy, so we had to carry them carefully causing more staining to our hands. On our arrival at the farm, we proudly showed Mrs Ladd the fruits of our labour which turned out to be only two half bags of fruit since my bag had mysteriously become empty! It was strange also that my lips had become twice as stained as the girls. Benny who had come into the house at that time, suggested that I should forego my share of pie as I had not contributed any fruit. I was relieved to learn that the suggestion hadn't been taken seriously when we all eventually enjoyed Mrs Ladd's whinberry pie topped with fresh cream.

I think Mrs Ladd must have spent most of her lifetime cooking and making cups of tea. Apart from the pot of 'cawl' which she attended to every day, she would always have something else cooking either on the griddle plate or in the oven. Although our meals were usually fairly basic there was always enough to eat and we were totally unaffected by rationing, though Mrs Ladd was always trying to stock up with tea and sugar for special occasions.

As on all the farms, three meals a day were eaten by all and in between times the kettle was always boiling on the stove for cups of tea. These were drunk first thing in the morning before milking and at morning and afternoon tea breaks and last thing at night. Tea was also made at any time for visitors, like family or friends dropping in or trades people, the vet or postman. Rene and I seldom drank tea but usually had milk. However, I'm sure our two spare tea rations were put to good use.

To provide something to accompany all this tea drinking, Mrs Ladd was kept busy at the stove baking biscuits and cakes in the oven and pancakes and Welsh cakes on the griddle plate over the fire. Bread and butter and cheese were also always placed on the table, but it was the baking of the bread that we liked watching the most.

This happened every Friday throughout the year, except Good Friday, and it was the temperature changes through summer and winter that were a challenge to Mrs Ladd, for it was critical for the dough to have the right warmth to rise to the exact degree and to the exact time.

First thing after breakfast the big baker's oven in the corner was fired. The wood had been stacked overnight by the stove to dry, for a good hot fire was essential in bread making. Then with sleeves rolled up Mrs Ladd would mix the flour and water into a dough and then adding the baker's yeast and some salt before giving it a good pummelling. By the time the dough had reached the required consistency beads of perspiration had formed on Mrs Ladd's forehead, which no doubt contributed to the flavour of the bread. Flour would become sprinkled over her apron and some would settle on her glasses and forehead where she had wiped the perspiration from her brow.

The dough was placed in two or three buckets, but only to half full in order to give the dough space to rise. Next came the critical time. In summer the buckets could be placed in the sun providing it was not too hot. Here they were rotated and kept from the shadows. In the winter the only warmth was near the fire where the buckets were placed. Again they were rotated to get an even warmth, the secret being to get all the dough to rise simultaneously to the correct level.

Usually Mrs Ladd timed it to perfection but the occasional disaster would occur when the bucket would get a little too warm and the dough would rise like a monster and spill from under the cloth that covered the buckets. If it had been too cold when Mrs Ladd lifted the cloth the dough would not have risen at all.

When everything was to Mrs Ladd's satisfaction the dough would be emptied out on to the table and pounded again and then put back into the buckets for a second rising. After another pummelling the dough would be formed into flat round loaves. Mrs Ladd would then check the fire and test the temperature of the oven by sticking her elbow into it. If all was satisfactory the round flat loaves were placed on the oven shelves.

It was not long before a delicious aroma proclaimed the first lot done and the oven would be refilled. Mrs Ladd always made sure that a small amount of dough was left over and this was made into a small loaf and cooked with the last batch. This was our treat and was eaten hot from the oven. Broken into pieces and smeared with fresh farm butter which melted quickly and ran down our fingers, we thought this was the best treat of all.

The bread was superb. It kept well in the coolness of the dairy and the crust was always crisp. It had a nutty flavour with a slightly smoky aroma, and it fascinated Rene and I to watch Mrs Ladd slice the bread and butter at meal times. She would hold the round flat loaf lengthwise against her bosom, thinly butter the bread, then, slicing towards herself with a huge sharp carving knife she would cut slice after slice of the thinnest bread and butter we had ever seen. Each piece was perfect, never broken or of uneven thickness, and each slice was arranged evenly to form a mountain of bread and butter on a special willow pattern plate.

Although we sometimes forgot what day of the week it was we always remembered it was Friday when we entered the house to be greeted by the smell of freshly baked bread.

Chapter 9

SUNDAY

We were always aware of Sundays too for, apart from milking, all work ceased on that day and it would have taken an impending disaster or major catastrophe to have altered this. After attending chapel in the mornings everybody enjoyed a day of rest. Preparations for Sunday, if possible, were made beforehand. Mrs Ladd would normally have food cooked in advance, and especially in summer when we would have cold meats and deserts and of course, the usual cawl in the winter.

Mr Ladd had his own Saturday night preparations and we watched in amazement the first time we saw him sharpen his cut-throat razor with a strop. He then placed a small shaving mirror on the table in the dim light of the oil lamp and proceeded to work his week's growth of whiskers into a lather. Then peering into the mirror he scraped away with the razor. What worried us was that somewhere in the lather was his wart and we breathed a sigh of relief when he finished his shaving with the wart still attached. Moving to the settle near the fire he would then take off his clogs and holey socks and soak his feet in a bowl of hot water. He suffered badly from corns and bunions and after a while he would set about trimming these also with the cut-throat and grimacing with pain as he did so. He would then sit and polish his best boots for the walk to the chapel in the morning.

As head of the family Mr Ladd always attended chapel but Mrs Ladd only went on special occasions since the long walk was rather distressing to her as she also suffered from corns and bunions. Megan, while still living at Dolrannog, would attend on a regular basis unless she had accompanied Wynfred to his chapel. Benny mostly disappeared on his bike.

Rene and I also attended unless the weather was too wet. We understood that Mrs Ladd appreciated some time to herself, so it wasn't long before we made our first attendance. This turned out to be a special occasion as the minister was returning to Dolrannog for lunch after the morning service. It also called for extra preparation on Saturday.

We had never been inside the parlour since our arrival and had only been given a peek through the door situated on the other side of the passage to the kitchen. It was seldom used and smelt damp and musty. Only on special occasions was the open fire ever lit and the room utilised. The parlour was not a large room and the heavy old fashioned furniture used up most of the space. A solid wood dining table and chairs were situated under the tiny front window and the upholstery on the matching chairs was mostly sagging. Against the back wall of the parlour stood a huge old dresser made from very dark wood. On this was displayed an array of crockery of various patterns and also some very delicate figurines amongst which lay the huge old family bible. Some heavily stuffed old fashioned armchairs stood facing the fire, all showing some signs of wear. A square pendulum clock stood silently on the mantle piece its hands stuck at 10'clock.

Although it was the middle of summer, the room felt damp and cold as I watched Megan and Rene set the table for the Sunday lunch. Firstly, a beautiful linen cloth was spread over the table. Though more yellow than white in places, the hand worked lace in the four corners looked outstanding even to my eyes. Matching linen serviettes were placed along side the heavy silver cutlery. Megan then dusted and placed fresh flowers around the room. Had the fire been lit, it would have looked quite cheerful.

Benny arrived with two plump chickens whose necks he had just wrung and within minutes, seated by the stove in the kitchen, Mrs Ladd and Megan had plucked one each. Then, with the quick thrust of a knife the guts were dropped out and eaten by the ever hungry dogs. The chickens were then stuffed and trussed before being placed in the dairy ready to be cooked for Sunday lunch.

A shower of rain had washed the countryside overnight. This helped settle the dust down the lane and the sun now had everything sparkling. Apart from the little birds darting in and out of the hedgerows and chirping loudly, all was at peace. It was hard to imagine that the world was at war. Our thoughts went back to the Sundays we had spent with our family; it was the only day our father didn't have to attend his office. Often we would visit our dear old Nan who lived quite close to the London docks or sometimes, uncles and aunts would visit us. We would all have a merry time together especially when everyone sat down to the traditional Sunday roast.

As we descended the open mountainside we couldn't help but compare this walk with the one we used to have to make at home, when we walked through the concrete jungles to our Sunday school.

Mr Ladd was making good progress in his soft Sunday boots and looked most distinguished in his black suit. A black tie was knotted over a crisp white shirt and a black bowler hat was set squarely on his head. Megan, who was walking alongside him, was dressed in a summer dress and a silk scarf covered her hair. Rene and I were wearing shoes and socks instead of sandals, and Rene had her hair tied back with a ribbon that matched her dress. I had started off with my hair damped down and combed back out of my eyes, but that didn't last long and it soon reverted to its untidy look.

It was a pleasant downhill walk through the beautiful Welsh countryside. A soft breeze kept the temperature from being too warm and we made good time. As we came closer to the chapel we met up with other groups of people to whom we were introduced and this would produce the inevitable barrage of questions about our home and parents. These were mostly directed at Rene, whose reply was then discussed in minute detail, in Welsh of course, ignoring our presence entirely. Even Megan seemed not to notice our discomfort.

I'm sure this was all quite unintentional and we realised that Welsh was their natural language but, because of our upbringing, we found this prying into our personal affairs most rude, and Rene especially found it quite upsetting. Fortunately, as time passed we became accepted by the locals and were questioned less often.

A hum of conversation could be heard from the small crowd that had gathered by the gateway to the chapel, rather like a swarm of bees waiting to enter a hive. Black was the predominant colour or the clothing and only the young unmarried and children wore any other. Rene and I were the only evacuees present; all the others were billeted in the village about five miles away. We were also the only people present who could not speak Welsh, indeed some of the older people struggled to speak English.

A flagstone path reached across the lawn to the doors of the chapel. Gravestones in various stages of neglect lined the pathway; the closest were free of weeds and the grass was trimmed and a few of the newest graves even sported vases of fresh flowers. The ones furthest from the path were almost hidden by long grass and weeds.

The chapel itself was small and plain, built of the common grey stone with the usual slate roof. It was rather square and box like and was situated on the floor of the valley, almost at its mouth, and the countryside surrounding it could only be described as beautiful.

The congregation filed into the chapel and sat in their regular places. Mr Ladd ushered us into the family pew. The inside of the chapel was quite austere and the small congregation about half filled it. The population was rather sparse in this area and there were other chapels scattered throughout the valley.

The minister was dressed in black. He was exceptionally tall and so thin as to be almost skeletal. He had wispy grey hair on top of his horse-like head, and bushy grey eyebrows that went up and down in rhythm as he spoke. But, it was his beady black eyes that made me feel uncomfortable because they seemed to penetrate one's innermost thoughts. He spoke at first very softly before shouting out at the congregation who responded with cries of 'hallelujah', and giving me quite a fright. There would be no sleeping or fidgeting in this service, and we followed Megan's lead as we stood, knelt or sat according to the custom.

Listening to a language we could not understand soon became boring but at one point the minister must have mentioned Rene and me and the war and everyone turned to look at us with murmurings of sympathy. This made Rene's cheeks turn pink. Then, a lady sporting a black bonnet sat herself down at the old harmonium and pumping away at the pedals produced an asthmatic introduction to a hymn which was immediately drowned out as the congregation burst into song.

There was no choir as such. The congregation was the choir and they all blended together from bass to soprano. Without a choirmaster they arranged themselves into parts. Sometimes the ladies sang on their own, sometimes just the men, but when singing together they reached such a crescendo that I swear I felt the floor move. I had never heard singing like it. It was nothing like the thin embarrassed singing I had experienced with my family in our local Church of England at home. This singing made everyone want to join in and in time even we did too. Although we never learned the meaning of the Welsh words we did learn parrot fashion and in time we were able to sing most of the traditional songs and hymns in Welsh. In a few weeks we had come to love the countryside and now the music, maybe this was the start of our integration.

After the service was over and everyone was gathered around talking, a girl about the same age as my sister approached us and introduced herself as Patty Salmon. She told us she lived on a farm nearby and from that moment she and Rene became close friends, which was great for Rene, but there seemed to be a dearth of boys of my age in the district.

People had started to disperse but we had to wait for the minister, so I explored the sound of running water I could hear nearby. Opposite the chapel, on the other side of the road, I discovered a small man-made pond. It was formed in cement with natural rocks surrounding it. It was quite deep and water flowed in from a natural stream at one end and overflowed out at the other. I was about to test the water when Megan grabbed me and told me it was a special holy place, where members of the congregation dressed in a white gown were baptised by being completely immersed in the water. Even in the sunshine of a summer's day it looked cold and threatening and I felt grateful that I had been christened just with a few drops of water on my head as a baby, and I certainly would not receive a dunking if I was ever confirmed.

The people eventually dispersed and I could not help but notice that they had all walked to the service. There was not a car or a pony to be seen, not even a bicycle. The minister briefly acknowledged Rene and me then led the way back up the mountain in deep discussion with Mr Ladd. Rene and I walked either side of Megan and Patty Salmon accompanied us part of the way.

On our arrival Mrs Ladd made a great fuss of the minister. We enjoyed the dinner although I didn't get my favourite piece of chicken and could have eaten more. It didn't take long for the cold fruit and custard to slip down, and it wasn't long either before my fidgeting had us excused from the table, with warnings not to get our clean clothes dirty. We were tired from our walk but felt we should keep outside till the parson left, so we sat in the sun and talked about the Sundays we enjoyed at home until we both retreated into our own thoughts.

We must have slept because a cool breeze had put goose bumps on us and we saw Mr Ladd walking down the lane with the parson. Megan and Mrs Ladd had cleared everything away and Mrs Ladd was nodding off by the fire. We changed our clothes and went to fetch the cows. The parlour door was now closed again until the arrival of the next guests.

Summer was almost at an end and the mornings became crisper and the days shorter as Autumn stealthily came upon us. We became aware that we had seen everything at its best; from now on things could only get worse.

We had now lived on the farm for two months and Rene and I agreed that it was a hard life for man and beast and seemingly for little return. We were not looking forward to our long walk to and from school every day, but at least we would hear English spoken, and not Welsh. The language difference was perhaps the hardest thing we had to bear, although homesickness still overcame us at certain times. Letters from our mother gave us hope, backed up by our prayers at night, which had become shorter and repetitive.

What upset Rene most of all was the way the animals

were treated, though never deliberately with cruelty, there were times when their treatment seemed callous to say the least. Rene was upset by little things such as when a calf she had reared was sold for veal, or a baby chick with a broken leg was put out of its misery when she wanted to try and heal it. When Prince was castrated and when the men were trying to put a spike through the pig's nose she was even more upset. She hated to see a chicken have its head chopped off or the lambs losing their tails. On one occasion Benny noticed a cow had a crooked horn which was almost growing into its eye. Grabbing a special tool which he locked onto the horn, and gripping it by the long handles, he twisted back and forth until finally the horn came free to reveal a bloody stump. The cow was crying out in agony and blood was running down its face. Rene burst into tears and called Benny a butcher. This hurt Benny and as we sat round the dinner table that night he asked if anybody knew of a different way to dehorn a cow or should he have left it as it was for the cow to go blind. Rene said nothing but turned red in the face. I just felt sorry for her.

We had few fears about the farm or the animals. We had been warned about snakes but had not seen any and I think it was the geese that frightened us most or more correctly, the head gander. The geese spent most of their time grazing in the fields and only received attention prior to Christmas when they were culled and fattened with grain.

Mrs Ladd said that if we ignored them they would not worry us but I chose, where possible, to walk around them rather than through the flock when the gander would put on a show and come too close for comfort.

I was also afraid of Benny's dog Rover and kept away from him. Lil, the sheep dog, was always friendly and the dogs down the lane, although they still barked as we walked by, did not bother to run out at us any more. I had learned to walk slowly around horses and to talk softly in the cow shed.

The turkey gobbler would turn bright red but not attack anyone passing, and a couple of the cockerels would strut around with their wattles bloated with blood, but mainly to impress the pullets.

We thought it strange that the poultry were left to make their own nests and find their own places to roost. The turkeys would roost high in the trees, to be blown out by strong winds and sustain broken wings or legs. The ducks and other birds with chicks had to rely on the dogs to keep the foxes away but out of a batch of fifteen baby ducks or chickens it was lucky if more than a couple reached maturity.

We had time to become familiar with the problems of farming high up on a mountain and through all the exercise we had lost weight but we were fitter and the skin on our arms and legs had become a healthy golden colour. We were well-treated and cared for and we loved the Welsh countryside but our hearts were forever with our parents and home.

Chapter 10

HORSE POWER

It was nearly time for us to attend school and to face the
reality of a daily walk down and back up the mountain, a
round journey of six miles every day in all weather. There
was some discussion about us being able to ride if
somewhere could be found to leave the ponies.
Conveniently, a group of gypsies had just camped on the
mountain nearby and, as was their custom, they visited the
nearest farms selling clothes pegs and props and offering to
tell fortunes and also trading in horses.

Mr Lad didn't usually entertain gypsies and said they
were only looking around to see what they could steal and
that the horses they were offering had been badly treated
and, undoubtedly, stolen. However, the local constable had
checked them out and found nothing amiss. So when the
gypsies offered him a nice looking pony at a bargain price,
Mr Ladd reluctantly bought it. Benny checked it over then
took it for a ride and returned saying that it went like the
wind. The pony was breathing heavily which was to be
expected, but was not at all distressed, and it was declared
sound of wind and limb.

Now I was never overkeen on horses. I had learned that

one end kicks and the other end bites. My sister, however, like most girls, became horse mad. It was decided that if we were going to ride to school everyday we had to learn to ride properly and we needed some practice. So that is how, after bringing back the milk churns one morning Turpin was fitted with a bridle, as was the new pony, Melon. Mona arrived astride Emrys's pony to take us on our first ride. None of us had saddles. There was only one belonging to the farm anyway, but it was deemed safer for us to ride bare back or rather on a chaff bag, so that in a fall we would not be dragged by a foot caught in a stirrup.

The Ladds lined up to wave us goodbye, with Mrs Ladd giving us instructions to keep together and to keep a tight rein, not to gallop and to keep away from the wild horses. As it turned out the opposite applied. The horses were reluctant to leave home, two of them having already done a morning's work, and it took all our energy to keep them moving. We only had one gate to negotiate and Mona helped us through with the warning that given half a chance the horses would bolt for home. Our destination was Maenclochog, a village five miles away on the opposite side of the valley, where Mona hoped to buy some material. We made our way down the mountain and along the road to the chapel then climbed up and over more open country without seeing any wild horses.

Mona was an excellent horsewoman and very confident. Rene and I slid stiffly off our horses and Mona checked that they were all securely tied to the rail or it would be a long walk home. We didn't spend long at the shop although Mona seemed to know everyone and they all wanted to chat, being curious about Rene and me. It had been a slow trip out and we wanted to be home before dusk. As it transpired we had no worries, apart from trying to stay on the horses, for they just wanted to go, eager to get home. We found that a canter or a gallop was far more comfortable than walking or a trot and much more exciting too with the wind whistling past our ears.

We arrived home safely and early and Mona was questioned by the Ladds. From the little we could understand the report was good so perhaps we were going to be allowed to ride to school after all. As I took my aching body up the stairs to bed I wasn't sure it was the best idea, and my tender bottom agreed with me.

Rene definitely became horse-mad, and would ride Turpin at every opportunity. She was allowed to harness and saddle him on her own and of course would groom him, which he didn't like, and feed him treats, which he accepted without acknowledgement. Benny was not impressed and warned Rene that Turpin was a working horse and should not be treated as a pet.

Mrs Ladd, Megan and I were standing at the back door watching Rene put Turpin through his paces. She had him going round the small paddock at a trot, first in one direction and then turning, in another. The gateway to the farmyard was always open and every time they passed Turpin would try and make for the stable but Rene kept a tight grip on the reins making him go round again. Now she urged him into a canter which made Mrs Ladd cry out a warning. This startled the horse who swerved and ran through the gateway, unseating Rene, who fortunately landed on grass and not rocks. She had landed heavily on one arm which she was now holding as she struggled to get to her feet. Tears of pain and disappointment flowed down her cheeks as we all rushed to help her. Mrs Ladd was almost hysterical saying that Rene could have been killed and she was lucky not to have caught her foot in the stirrup. The story of course was repeated to Benny and Mr Ladd with more embellishments. A further inspection of Rene's arm, and a soaking in cold water was followed by a trip to the doctor. A towel was made into a rough sling to support Rene's arm for the walk to the village accompanied by Megan and me. It was a painful journey for Rene and conversation was kept to the minimum.

The doctor's diagnosis was a green stick fracture and after the arm was bandaged and put into a proper sling we made our weary way back home. By resting her arm the swelling went down and in a few days the sling was no longer needed and the arm made a perfect recovery.

We awoke the next morning to fire on the mountain and were told that the gypsies always burnt the gorse and bracken when they moved on so that more grass would grow for their next camp. Apparently, the pony Melon had moved on with them for there was no more talk of riding horses to school and we never saw Melon again.

A sense of urgency prevailed as harvest time drew nearer. A close watch was kept on the weather, for a sudden summer storm could ruin the crops, and this would create problems in trying to feed the animals through winter.

Benny had been busy checking the hay-rake and mower. The axles were packed with grease and all other moving parts well oiled. With a file Benny had sharpened the six foot blade of the mower, tooth by tooth, and I had turned the handle of the heavy round whetstone on which he sharpened the scythe and sickles.

Beds of brush had already been laid for the hay-stacks to prevent water seepage from the ground, and green rushes had been gathered from near the well and placed ready for thatching the stacks to prevent any damage from rain.

The local farmers formed themselves into groups, quickly moving from farm to farm to cart the hay. Some would arrive with just a pitchfork, others would arrive with a horse and cart. They worked in teams and although there was rivalry to see who carted the biggest loads of hay, they worked together in a most congenial manner.

Hay-making started after much discussion between Benny and Mr Ladd. Inspection of the crop and a keen observance of the skies, checking for any sign of rain, became the order of the preceding days.

The first preparation was to slice a swath around the hedgerow of the field to be cut, which would otherwise be flattened by the horse drawn mower on its first lap. Everyone joined in this task, the men cutting with scythes, the women with sickles. This hay was then raked to one side, a job safe enough for Rene and me to lend a hand with.

This was not only a busy time for Mrs Ladd, having to feed all the extra helpers, but also a worrying time. She had already warned Rene and me to keep out of the way of the machinery and on no account were we to touch the scythes or sickles. Then, looking me straight in the eye, she went on to illustrate her warnings with gory tales of children having feet cut off with one stroke of a scythe, and of others impaled on the tines of the hay-rake, or churned up in the mower. Nobody else seemed to have heard of these events but at least I survived the harvest in one piece!

Benny had Prince harnessed to the heavy mower. Without springs, the iron wheels gave him an uncomfortable ride perched on the hard metal seat. Guiding Prince with the reins in one hand he controlled the height of the blade by means of a lever in the other. Skill and timing were essential in avoiding the many rocks that lay hidden in the hay.

As usual Benny succeeded in cutting the hay quickly, cleanly and without mishap. He looked back with pride on completion, well pleased with the neat rows lying parallel on the ground. If the hay had not been dried out enough, or had become wet with rain or dew, it had to be turned over. When the time was right it was carted quickly into the hay guard and stacked. Benny, having quickly collected the hay into mounds with Turpin pulling the hay rake, now had his work cut out. Trying to build a perfect haystack, and at the same time trying to keep up with the carters who were anxious to finish and get on to the next farm, gave him no rest at all.

Corn was harvested in a similar manner except that after it had been cut and was lying in rows everyone helped to gather it into sheaves. These were tied with a plait hastily made from a few of the stalks, then fifteen sheaves were made into a stack in such a manner as to prevent water damage and to allow the wind to dry the corn. The women were quicker than the men at this task and I was not successful in tying even one sheaf without it falling apart, though Rene had seemed to get the hang of it. After a few days when the corn was deemed to be ripe the sheaves were carted into the hay guard and also stacked by Benny.

All this created a lot of hard work but the men also had some fun when Benny had almost finished mowing a field of hay or corn. The area of corn standing diminished each time the mower made a lap, and any rabbits who were caught out of the burrows at the start of mowing, now had very little cover to hide in. As Benny made the last cuts the rabbits had no option but to run the gauntlet of men and dogs across the mown field to their burrows in the hedgerow. For a few moments there was mayhem with rabbits running in all directions, some straight into the blades of the mower. With dogs barking madly and shotguns firing wildly it was soon over. Miraculously, the rabbits were the only ones to suffer death or injury as the men, who were all laughing uproariously called off their dogs.

Rene was upset as the injured rabbits were put out of their misery, and I joined her in cheering any that escaped in one piece down into their burrows, much to the amusement of the onlookers.

There was much rivalry between the farmers to see who could make the best hay-stack and this created many good-hearted arguments, but Benny would always stand defiant and defend his masterpiece against all comers. The stacks stood in the open so it was most important for the hay to be kept dry. Wet stacks became self combustible as intense heat could build up from mouldy hay compressed in the middle of the stack.

The stack resembled a small cottage in size, the sides sloping outward to the thatched roof to help shed the rain. The corners were square and the whole stack was combed with a large home-made wooden rake.

Benny was extremely good at thatching, taking too much time, according to Mr Ladd and turning it into an art form rather than just a practical means of weather proofing. Many a country cottage was less well thatched than Benny's stacks, and he was justifiably proud of them, taking great delight in showing them off to anyone who came to the farm. It must have caused him some disappointment when the time came to demolish them.

It was customary for each farm to put on a spread after the last of the crop was safely gathered in and the one I remember most took place at Tre-fach, the large farm on the other side of the valley.

Mr Ladd was taking Prince and the heavy old hay cart to help at Tre-fach for the day, in return for their help earlier at Dolrannog, and he asked me if I would like to accompany him. It was still cool and early in the morning when we set off down the mountainside and it was more comfortable to walk down the now familiar lane than ride in the cart and risk splinters.

It turned out to be a hot day even though summer would soon change to autumn and this was the last day of harvesting for the year. We joined about a dozen other men in a paddock at least twice as big as any at Dolrannog and there were several other horse-drawn carts being loaded with sheaves of corn as we arrived. At first I led Prince from stack to stack as a couple of men threw the sheaves up to Mr Ladd on their pitch forks. The cart had wooden racks extending the cart at the rear and at the front over Prince's rump. Mr Ladd carefully arranged the sheaves, stalks out and ears in, so that the ever heightening load would not topple. When the load was high enough Mr

Ladd, with some difficulty, managed to reach the ground and we made our way to the hay guard. The cart was soon emptied as Mr Ladd and a couple of others threw the sheaves up on to the ever growing stack, to be arranged by a couple of other men.

Jugs of cold water were on hand as the day hotted up and these were not only to drink from but were splashed over itchy arms or faces to remove the dust.

After a couple of loads Mr Ladd, who was having trouble climbing on and off the cart, asked me if I thought I could stack the load which I did. I soon got the hang of it, making sure I kept away from the prongs of the pitch forks that at times came too close for comfort.

We continued in this manner until almost sundown when a cheer went up as the last sheaf was carted away. We had had a couple of short breaks when hot mugs of tea and sandwiches were served but now I was exhausted, aching in every limb, sore from sunburn and itching all over. But all this lifted from me when every one told me what a great job I had done. Proudly, I took my place among the men as we went inside the farmhouse and sat down on benches drawn up to a long white pine table, laden with food.

We all crowded into the small room where a dresser was the only other piece of furniture. I did notice how clean everything was; even the walls and ceiling had been freshly limed. Ladies waited on us, filling our mugs from big enamel jugs, not with tea this time, but homemade beer, and with encouragement from the men they filled my mug too.

The beer was good and I quickly decided it was a drink I could grow to be quite fond of! I surprised myself at the speed with which I had emptied my mug only to have it promptly refilled. Fortunately, hunger struck and I set about satisfying the pangs before drinking any more beer. A home cooked ham took my eye amidst a multitude of other platters of meat, cheese, butter and bread, hard boiled eggs, faggots, jacket potatoes, pancakes, Welsh cakes, various other cakes, sweet and savoury, pies, stewed fruit custard and cream. I soon felt full as people kept pressing food onto me and filling my mug with more beer. My eyes were getting heavy when a burst of song suddenly brought me awake. This soon gathered momentum as everyone joined in, blending together like a well rehearsed choir. I was wide awake now as the men started to beat time by thumping on the table as the song reached its climax, only to cease in amazement as the ceiling started to disintegrate and lumps of plaster landed on the table. Now everyone was rolling around with laughter as they realised that the room had been freshly limed only the day before and the plaster in the ceiling had not had time to dry. The vibrations of their singing and thumping had literally brought the house down!

I was not aware of the trip home, but I suspect it was Prince who did most of the navigating as Mr Ladd had also become very tired. I was stiff and sore when I woke up the next day but the pain eased at the breakfast table when Mr Ladd told everyone that I had worked like a real farm hand. I was glad we were outside when Rene added that I had come to bed smelling like one too!

Chapter 11

STEAM ENGINE

Any illusions of manhood that I may have had after my day
of toil at Tre-fach were quickly shattered on the following
Sunday.

It was a warm afternoon. Rene was away with Mona and
the others were having a siesta after the morning attendance
at chapel. I became bored with amusing myself outside and
decided to go inside to see if anyone was awake yet.

Cobblestones formed the short path from the front gate
to the house so my sandals made little noise. I stepped onto
the front porch and as usual Lil, the black and white sheep
dog was asleep under the left bench and Rover, Benny's
hunting dog, was under the opposite bench.

I paused to look at the dogs and Lil gave a desultory wag
of her tail so I stopped and gave her a pat on the head.
Rover, who I thought looked more like a wolf than a dog,
did not wag his tail. However, wishing to be impartial I bent
over to give him a pat too. I received a deep throated growl
in response to my friendly gesture. I hastily withdrew my
hand, but before I could stand up straight he sprang at me.
He knocked me over onto my back and leapt on top of me.
He then grabbed me between my eyes with his teeth and

shook me. I screamed and the dog ran off. Holding my face and with blood flowing between my fingers I dashed inside. Megan took me into her arms and tried to comfort me, but I couldn't stop crying.

I was crying , not only because of the shock and pain, but for all the times I had been hurt or frightened but had hidden my feelings and held back my tears. From my earliest years my father had told me that it was not manly to cry. My mother was not a demonstrative person either and physical expressions of love were rare in our family.

Now Megan was holding me to her and, even though she had placed a wet cloth over my face, I could still smell the sweetness of her skin as I lay against her shoulder. I could feel her softness as she held me close to her, comforting me. I just let my tears fall freely, content to be a young boy.

Mr and Mrs Ladd hurried downstairs to see what all the fuss was about and Mrs Ladd instantly prayed to God on seeing all the blood. Mr Ladd questioned Megan as to what had happened.

I didn't look too bad when my sister arrived back a short while later. Megan had cleaned me up and I was lying on the old couch with a cold wet cloth over my nose. The bleeding had abated but even so, my sister turned white and I thought she would faint.

I made a quick recovery but was left with one rather nasty tooth mark on my nose very close to my right eye. The bleeding had stopped but there was now a fear of infection so a trip to the doctor was deemed necessary. There was only one way to get to the village and that was by walking, of course.

So Megan, Rene and I set off on the walk we were getting to know so well. Dr Davies didn't seem at all put out by having his Sunday afternoon disturbed and talked to me in a very kind manner, telling me that the wound would have to be cauterised. He warned me that it would hurt, and it did. But I had done my crying so I gritted my teeth and held back my tears. The walk back to Dolrannog was a slow affair with many stops for rests. I was exhausted and my nose was sore and after a light tea I was thankful to make my way to bed. As I said my goodnights to everyone I became aware that Benny was looking at me intently with a questioning look in his eye. I had no doubt that I had a trial to contend with tomorrow.

I had a restless night which could have been because of the shock or over tiredness or my guilty conscience and I woke up late with a headache and two black eyes. I went downstairs where Benny was still sitting at the breakfast table not looking very happy at all, so I asked him if Rover had returned home. I was shocked when he told me that Rover would not be going anywhere as he had been shot. Mr Ladd had not wanted to take the risk of Rover attacking anyone else and decreed that he should be destroyed. Benny had apparently wanted to wait to hear what I had to say as he felt that the dog would have had a reason for doing what he'd done. But Mrs Ladd had also insisted and now Benny was waiting to interrogate me.

I felt full of remorse. I knew I was to blame for Rover's death even though, as I honestly stated, I did not actually touch or talk to him. I knew that had I obeyed the order to leave the dogs alone, Rover would still be alive. I swore to Benny that I had not touched Rover and although he believed me I knew that he felt he hadn't got the full story.

To cheer me up, the next morning Mr Ladd told me that a steam engine was soon coming to Dolrannog. Seeing the look of surprise on my face he went on to explain that the engine was like a big steam roller with wheels instead of a roller. Pulling a large box-like threshing machine which had iron wheels, it travelled from farm to farm to thresh the wheat that the farmers had harvested and stacked ready.

I wondered how big the machine could be as the lane was very narrow and at one point was further reduced by two large rocks that had once formed a gateway. Mr Ladd assured me that Mr Owens had been driving the engine all his life and could put it through the eye of a needle. So, on the day it was due to arrive, I decided that I would see this for myself. Rene was not interested in steam engines but hurrying through my breakfast I told Mrs Ladd that I was going down the lane to watch the engine arrive. She thought this was a good idea and said that Mr Owens was bound to give me a ride back.

It was a lovely morning and an easy walk of about a mile to the two rocks but, after my experience with Rover, it took some courage to keep walking when the neighbouring farms dogs ran out barking at me. On arriving at the rocks I looked around. Above, the mountain did not look at all threatening with the sun shining on the huge granite rocks that formed the peaks. Down across the valley, the patchwork of fields were still lush and predominantly green. Smoke from the chimneys of a few scattered cottages rose vertically through the clear air to indicate that not the slightest of breezes would cool the valley on this morning. Indeed, a lone black hawk had to work hard as it hovered high in the sky, having failed to find a thermal to rest on, while it waited for its prey to appear.

Turning my attention to the two flat rocks I found some holes that had obviously been used in hanging the now defunct gate. Also, on one of the rocks an arrow had been carved, a mark I had also noticed on other predominant rocks.

I heard it before I could see it. The unmistakable sounds of a real steam engine forewarned me of its impending arrival. Then I saw the white puffs of steam rising into the air where they were briefly suspended to form a chain like a pearl necklace before vanishing.

As the engine came closer, I jumped up and down in great excitement in the middle of the lane. I expected it to stop or at least slow down before squeezing between the two rocks. However, a blast from the whistle caused me to leap into the hedgerow from which point of safety I watched it go by. I could feel the warmth of its fire as the monster went by without slowing down at all, passing between the rocks with less than an inch to spare, and its large iron wheels grinding over the stony surface.

It had a high smoke-stack and a square wooden roof covered the footplate where Mr Owens stood holding the wheel with one hand and an oily rag in the other. Behind him was the coal bunker. The engine was obviously his pride and joy. The black paint and brass work shone whereas the threshing machine looked dusty, its woodwork dry and in need of paint.

I stood watching it disappear around the next bend before running after it belatedly realising that I was not to have a ride home.

When I eventually caught up with it the threshing

machine had already been positioned alongside the stack of corn with the engine facing it. The men were manhandling the big black drive-belt over the fly-wheel to form a figure of eight before positioning the other loop over the pulley wheel of the thresher. With some delicate manipulation of the controls Mr Owens eased the engine into position to give the correct tension on the belt. Then, warning me to stand well clear, he placed both hands on the big clutch lever and gently set the belt in motion. A small cloud of dust rose from the threshing machine as it came to life, the clickerty-clack of its innards giving way to a steady hum as the correct revolutions were attained.

Mrs Ladd had already warned me to stay away from the machine, telling me one of her tales about someone who had slipped into one and had come out the other end as minced meat.

A few neighbours had come to lend a hand and were standing around pretending to criticise Benny's beautiful thatchwork which he was now pulling down from the stack taking care not to let any of the thatch contaminate the stack of wheat.

Bags were attached to the back of the thresher to catch the wheat. When all was ready, two men took positions on the flat roof of the machine on one side of a hatch while another two men were ready with pitch forks on top of the stack of wheat. Since the stack was slightly higher it was not hard work to toss the sheaves from it to the men on the thresher who untied them and fed them into the hatch in an even flow. Too much at one time would cause the machine to clog, wet sheaves would do the same and the men worked in a steady rhythm with an eye on the clouds above.

What went on inside this machine was a miracle for the farmers, long before combine harvesters became common. The grain that was extracted poured into sacks hanging from the back which, when filled were stacked in the barn. The best was put aside for seed to be sown the following year, and some kept separate to be taken to the mill later on to be ground into flour. The poorest quality was used to feed the chickens. All that was left over was straw and this was used for bedding the cows and horses during the worst part of the winter.

As the stack shrank, the men had to throw the sheaves up to the men on the thresher. I just stood staring at Mr Owens as he wiped the brass gauges or threw the occasional shovel of coal under the boiler. How I longed to be standing next to him on the footplate. Then it happened; Mr Owens climbed down and came across to me and asked if I would like to join him in the warmth of the footplate as it was starting to get chilly. My excitement was short-lived though as he pressed a shilling into my hand saying that he had run out of cigarettes and would I first go to the shop for him. My heart sank. The nearest shop was Ty'n Rhos which was half way to chapel, a round trip of three miles and I had just walked two miles! I checked to see how much of the stack remained, concerned that everything would be over before my return. I then set off on my errand, harbouring an intense feeling of frustration. I made good time on the downhill journey to the shop, running most of the way and arriving out of breath only to find that Miss Jones was reluctant to sell cigarettes to a small boy. She finally accepted my money but warned me that she would check my story with Mrs Ladd and made me promise not to smoke any on the way home.

Fearful that everything would be finished before I arrived back, I really pushed myself on the uphill return journey, and arrived a little distressed. I soon recovered when I found everything still working. I handed Mr Owens his cigarettes and change. He kept his promise and told me to climb aboard.

He made me stand on the left side away from the heavy flywheel that was spinning around driving the big black belt. He explained that if the belt were to snap there was no knowing where it would end up and it could even take off my head. He also showed me the controls and how the coal had to be spread evenly over the fire to keep up steam.

My moment of glory came after the last sheaf had been thrown into the threshing machine, the big black belt stowed away and everything hooked up in place and ready to go. I was allowed to drive or, more honestly, help drive the monster from the hay guard. As I pulled the cord to blow the whistle, Mr Owens eased the clutch in and with a shudder of power and a belch of smoke we were off. As we entered the farmyard even the ganders took flight and there was an immediate fall in egg production as the usually peaceful farmyard was evacuated by all living things. Another blast from the whistle brought Mrs Ladd running as we stopped outside the door. Reluctantly climbing down from the engine, I joined the other men over a cup of tea.

Getting ready for bed that evening I was feeling exhausted so my ablutions were even more perfunctory than usual and my prayers shorter.

Chapter 12

NEW SCHOOL

Our lives changed dramatically from the day school started. The summer had passed by at a leisurely pace giving us time to become familiar with our new surroundings. The days had been long and warm but now a hint of autumn was giving the early morning a certain freshness and warning us of times to come.

We had woken early and, not feeling very hungry at breakfast, we were ready to leave for school ahead of time. We were dressed in the same clothes we had worn on Sundays and wearing shoes and socks, our sandals having finally disintegrated beyond repair. My ablutions had been supervised by Mrs Ladd so I looked and smelt reasonably clean. Rene always managed to keep herself looking fresh, in spite of the lack of modern plumbing.

In a canvas haversack, Mrs Ladd had packed our sandwiches and milk in two glass bottles with spring loaded stoppers. We would have to take turns in carrying it. As the sky was clear we decided not to take our raincoats even though Mrs Ladd warned us of the sudden weather changes at this time of the year.

Megan entered the house carrying a jug full of cream

just as we were about to leave, so she accompanied us as far as the bend in the lane, then we were on our own. Our first obstacle was the dogs at the next farm down and as usual they ran out at us barking savagely. After my encounter with Rover I felt very frightened but I tried not to show it and did my best to reassure Rene.

We were familiar with the journey to the village but with our minds preoccupied with the events of the coming day we took little notice of our surroundings, although I did check New England for signs of life as we walked by. We continued down the road and as we passed the cottages, people would wave to us from their doorway. One lady, whom we recognised, actually ran to her front gate to bombard us with questions. We pretended not to understand and kept on walking ever downwards, passing the ruins of the ancient castle and then through the village to the hall.

Full of anticipation, we made good time on our downhill walk as we wished to arrive early on our first day at school. Memories of our first night in Wales came flooding back as we shyly joined other children who were gathered around the open doors at the side entrance to the hall. We did not know anybody as they were not from a school attended by either Rene or me in England. We had merely been tacked on at the last moment before evacuation when things were a little chaotic.

Not being one for standing still I decided on some reconnaissance. The front entrance, which looked little used, was set in a fancy façade but otherwise the hall looked like any other village hall, rather boring. I walked to the back of the building where some boys were playing ball in a small tree lined area, which also contained a row of four toilets to one side. I immediately felt the need to visit these and anticipated the luxury of using a proper toilet. On opening the door I was shocked by the stench, for these were pan toilets and not flush toilets. I was not familiar with these but what was worse was that someone had neglected to empty them. Disappointed, I joined another boy who was watering a tree then made my way back to tell my sister about my sickening discovery.

Eventually we were called into line and on entering the hall were ticked against a register and our Christian names were printed on a label and attached to us. We were then, by age, formed into two groups with about twenty in each. The senior group, which included my sister, was allocated the area in front of the stage and was supervised by the head teacher, a Miss Foy.

The other group was allocated space at the other end of the hall. At first there was utter confusion for although there were plenty of chairs there were not enough tables, and both groups were audible and visible to each other.

I found myself sitting at a table at the end furthest from the teacher and opposite me sat a girl who kept staring at me. Between us, seated on chairs at the end of the table were two boys. Although strangers to me they all seemed acquainted with each other and spoke with the same accent. The teacher was calling for quiet so that she could start reading us a story.

The girl had straight red hair cut in the shape of a pudding basin, and her white skin was covered in freckles. She kept staring at me with her dark brown eyes then sliding forward on her chair she gave me an encouraging smile. Unaware of the game she was playing, I just remained seated with a puzzled expression on my face. The boy next to me told me the girl wanted me to look under the table, which I did. Through a maze of legs belonging to the table and the chairs and the children, I could see she had lifted her dress and, by putting her finger inside the elastic of the leg of her knickers she was now exposing to me that which every girl's mother normally instructed her darling daughter to keep well covered. I was shocked, as I had never seen an undressed female, not even a glimpse of my mother or my sister as we were a conservative type of family. Banging my head on the table in the process I hastily resumed my seat in astonishment. I became aware of the teacher's eyes on me. I tried to act nonchalantly, keeping my eyes away from the girl and making an effort to concentrate on what the teacher was saying. But I was not left in peace for long, a sudden elbow in the ribs caused me to turn to the boy nearest me, who informed me it was my turn to expose myself to the girl as she really liked me. There was no way I could comply with her command; I was far too embarrassed and there was no doubt that the teacher was becoming aware of some questionable behaviour in our vicinity. I was in a real predicament as the boys kept urging me more loudly and calling attention to the fact that she had shown me hers and I was now expected to show her mine.

An idea came to mind and pretending to acquiesce, I slid one of my hands inside the waistband of my trousers, pretending to undo my buttons with the other, then I poked a finger out of my fly hoping it resembled the real thing. It didn't and she wasn't fooled for a second! Our heads were nearly touching under the table and she gave me a look of utter contempt as we resumed our proper places. From then on she completely ignored me. She obviously didn't give second chances.

I was completely confused by the girl's behaviour and asked Rene for an explanation as we walked home. She too seemed embarrassed and her only reply was to walk faster, making conversation impossible. I didn't know what part of London these kids came from, but I soon found out that they were more worldly wise than Rene and me.

Some semblance of order had been gained by playtime. Rene and I were both hungry after our small breakfast and long walk and so, decided to eat half our lunch. We had assured Mrs Ladd that one cheese sandwich and a small bottle of milk would be sufficient for the day but we now realised that we had made a poor estimate. The milk in the glass bottles tasted sour after the shaking up it had received on the long walk, and I reckoned mine was about to turn into butter. However, for some unknown reason, we never did ask for more lunch and always assured Mrs Ladd that we had sufficient.

Our second period was better organised than the first but I found it most disconcerting to be able to hear two different teachers at the same time. Later, as supplies became more plentiful we were able to have quiet periods of drawing, writing or reading and the problem lessened, but it always seemed easier to concentrate on the other class's lessons.

As school ended on the first day Rene and I felt tired and hungry as we started back to Dolrannog. We were caught in a shower of rain but the uphill climb kept us warm. We had been rather disappointed in having to make do with the hall and we were not in a good mood as we came to the cottages where, sure enough, the inquisitive woman was waiting for us at her gate. Once again she asked us about our parents and our home but I was totally surprised when Rene, red of face, turned on the woman and told her to mind her own business and called her a nosy parker.

As the woman disappeared into her home, slamming the door behind her, Rene and I burst out laughing. We arrived at Dolrannog tired and hungry but once again we had to answer questions as the family was anxious to know what we had done on our first day at school.

Lying in bed that night I began to have doubts about our ability to cope with the long school days ahead, and added a prayer to God for a quick ending to the war. For the first time, we had to be woken up by Mrs Ladd in the morning.

She came into our bedroom carrying the clothes we had worn the day before, which were wet when we arrived home. Mrs Ladd had placed them around the fire to dry overnight but they still felt damp as we put them on, and on looking out of our little window we could see it was raining again. We wore our raincoats to school that day, but they only kept us dry for half of the way before they became sodden and we became wet through.

At first the Autumn weather was quite mild with some fine days on which we would take our time walking home. Exploring the hedgerows we would find the last blackberries, and the hazel nuts were now ripe enough to eat. We were well aware though that winter was approaching, as the days grew shorter and the weather worsened; then our daily walk became the bane of our existence.

The downhill run to school was not so bad when we became expert short term weather forecasters, and by leaving a little earlier or later, we were sometimes able to make the journey between squalls and showers. We made some very quick times running down hill, and almost equalled the Olympic record according to the clock at Dolrannog and the clock in the hall. As nobody had a watch and we had no way of synchronising the clocks, we never mentioned our athleticism to any one. To amuse ourselves we would sometimes make up fantasies or play games, but most of the time we were too tired or out of breath to talk.

Because of the steepness of the climb, our walk home was much harder and took much longer. Our outer garments were usually still damp when we put them on, even though they had been draped around the kerosene heater in the hall all day. Whatever the weather we couldn't afford to hang around the hall for long if we wanted to get home before dark. So, Rene and I worked out a plan, mentally splitting the three mile walk into three parts.

The first part was leaving the village and following the road back to New England. Although having some of the steepest hills, this section had plenty of space to shelter from sudden squalls unlike the next section which was the track across the face of the mountain and was completely exposed until it reached the farm land. This was not the place to be caught out in a storm and we were always pleased when this section was behind us. The lane to Dolrannog was the last section with the walls and hedgerows giving some protection on both sides. It was also where we had to contend with the dogs every day.

Friday was the best day of the week for us, as we trudged the last yards to the house. Lil would greet us at the porch and on opening the door our senses would be invaded by the warmth of the fires and the smell of freshly baked bread. Mrs Ladd would call us to her, telling us to get out of our wet clothes and come to the fire, where she handed us hot bread straight from the oven and spread with farm butter. As we sat next to Mrs Ladd on the old couch, next to the fire, she would dry my hair and tell Rene and me to sleep late in the morning.

By this time school had already been forgotten and Monday was a year away. As I licked the butter from my fingers and watched the changing patterns in the fire my thoughts would again turn to home.

Chapter 13

CHRISTMAS

Almost six months had passed since we had last seen our parents. The war was dragging on and there was no mention of our returning home. Christmas was approaching but we had already been told that New Year was also a major celebration in south-western Wales, and that was often celebrated on a different day, keeping to the old traditional calendar and celebrating the New Year on the 13th January. We had not had a letter from our parents for a while so we were feeling a bit down in the dumps as we walked home, wet, as usual, from the rain.

Lil gave us a desultory wag of her tail as we passed through the porch and entered the farm house where we found Mrs Ladd waiting for us in a great state of excitement and waving a letter in her hand. She told us our parents were coming to see us and handed Rene the letter to read aloud, which she managed to do in spite of shaking hands.

We learned that Dad had been given a week's leave over Christmas and, if accommodation could be found for them in the village, they would try to spend some time with us but adding that this depended on the availability of trains. Air raids and bomb damage had caused havoc with the timetables, and so to avoid disappointing us our mother had asked Mrs Ladd not to tell us until the final arrangements had been made, but the chances of Mrs Ladd keeping a secret were about as likely as pigs flying.

This news caused much discussion around the fire that evening and even Rene and I were included. We were asked a lot of questions, such as what sort of bed our parents slept in and what bathing facilities we had in our home. It became obvious that for our parents to stay anywhere other than Dolrannog was unthinkable, but how to accommodate them was another matter.

Time now was of the essence and a letter was posted the next day stating that arrangements had been made for them to stay at Dolrannog over Christmas. All we had to do now was to wait for them to confirm the date.

The major problem though was that Dolrannog had no toilet, and the thought of Captain and Mrs Foskett baring their backsides behind a hedge in the middle of a Welsh winter, was quite unthinkable. Chamber pots under the bed took care of the shortcomings through the night. Unfortunately, the accompanying sound effects would travel through the matchwood thin dividing walls of the bedrooms, often inspiring Benny to pass a ribald remark. This would send everyone into fits of laughter which were eventually quietened by a mild rebuke from Mr Ladd. There was only one solution, a proper toilet had to be built and soon.

The construction proved relatively quick and simple. It was made from second hand corrugated iron over a wooden frame and when finished it resembled a sentry box with an ill fitting door. As expected Benny came up

151

with many comments during construction, especially when he had to cut the hole in the seat with a saw, leaving splinters around the rough edges, which he later smoothed around with a rasp and sandpaper.

A flush toilet was out of the question and the bucket system had seemed the only alternative but Benny then came up with one of his brilliant ideas. If the toilet could be sighted over a flowing stream the problem would be solved as all the effluence would, in theory, be carried away. The question of what would happen in the summer when the stream became a trickle went unanswered, time was running out.

The toilet needed to be near the house and preferably out of sight, and after much discussion there seemed to be only one place suitable, and that was behind the wall next to the pigsty. There a hole in the wall allowed all the water that ran down the slope of the farmyard to drain away, forming a stream which followed the wall along to the next paddock where it made a sharp turn and followed the hedgerow down to the valley and the river below.

But one more problem remained, there was no way over the wall. It was a low wall, and easy for me to scale, but it was impossible for Mrs Ladd and unacceptable for our parents. So three large thick pieces of slate were found and these were driven between the rocks in the wall forming rough steps. There was no handrail.

After much pushing and shoving the toilet was fixed in its place although at a slight angle. Flat stones were laid on the floor which had now turned to mud, and with a last flourish a nail was hammered into the frame to hold whatever paper could be found.

Mrs Ladd was called to inspect the end result. She had to walk from the front of the house, across the yard to the steps in the wall which she managed with some difficulty, then walk through the long grass behind the pigsty before flopping, somewhat out of breath, on the seat. The whole thing rocked alarmingly before settling down on a slightly greater slant.

Mrs Ladd became conscious of the sound of water beneath her and immediately shut the door before the noise increased. Benny was about to make some comment about flooding but a quick word from Mr Ladd changed his mind. Stepping out through the door Mrs Ladd voiced her approval but told Benny to cut the long grass as it would be wet for people's shoes. Of course, the real test was yet to come, but when it was my turn to inspect the structure the best thing I noticed was the view from the open door which extended right across the valley to the hills beyond.

The toilet never really worked though; tests with paper showed that the volume of water was never going to disperse much of anything. Even after frantic digging and deepening of the ditches the bits of paper still stuck around the toilet, much to the perplexity of Benny and the ducks. It was finally decided that the toilet would have to be converted to the obnoxious bucket system, and that was completed in haste, literally hours before our parents were due to arrive.

The last few days of school dragged on. Miss Foy did her best to create a festive mood in the hall; we made Christmas cards to send home and sang the obligatory Christmas carols around the traditional scene of the nativity before breaking up for the holidays. On arriving at

Dolrannog on our last day of school our suspense was replaced with anticipation on finding a letter waiting for us. Our parents were still coming.

The last part of their journey would be by bus then taxi, so they could not give us an exact time of arrival, in fact they could not guarantee the exact day and warned us not to worry if they did not arrive at all, as they had been told that the railway tracks were badly damaged in some areas! Of course, the nearest telephone to us was in the village so no contact could be made that way.

We would have spent the next few days just staring out the window waiting for the local taxi but Megan kept us busy instead. In fact, I had never seen so much activity in the house. All the bedrooms were cleaned, sheets changed on the beds as Mr and Mrs Ladd relinquished their bedroom to the Captain and his lady. This was the largest bedroom and had a wardrobe, dressing table and a wash stand on which a basin and a pitcher of water stood ready. Hot water would be brought up from the boiler downstairs as required. The po, washed and polished, was placed in position under the bed!

Rene and I kept our little bedroom with its double bed but where the Ladd family all slept I have no idea, as the house only had three bedrooms.

Downstairs Mrs Ladd was creating a convincing imitation of Dante's Inferno with ovens ablaze as bread, cakes, pies and other creations were cooked and all amidst the flying feathers of a goose she was plucking and that Benny had just killed. A ham was cooking in the black cauldron suspended over the fire, adding steam to the smoke. Megan and Rene were busy getting the parlour dusted and then decorated with tinsel and greenery. I was busy carrying in the wood for the fires, even Benny kept coming into the house to check the small barrel of ale that had been held back from harvest. This was Christmas.

The evening before the grand arrival, the big brass pan that the animals drank from was brought in from the farmyard and placed before the fire. This was also used for making the homebrew, but tonight it became a bath. Buckets of cold water from outside were poured in followed by hot from the boiler and then by me. Mrs Ladd set about me from top to toe with a scrubbing brush in one hand and a block of carbolic soap in the other. I had been a sort of grey colour when I got into the tub but had changed to a bright shade of pink by the time I got out! I lay in my clean pyjamas in our clean bed waiting for Rene to come so we could say our prayers together. We prayed for our parents' safety and thanked God for our warmth and comfort, but we were far too excited to sleep.

They arrived at mid-day the next day, which was Christmas Eve. At the sound of the taxi Rene and I raced outside ignoring to rain. The Ladds gathered in the porch and waited for us to finish our greetings. We were never a family to show a lot of emotion and the rain dampened our ardour but even so my mother had tears in her eyes as she cuddled me and kissed me, and I even received a pat on the back from Dad after we had shaken hands. What struck me though was the change in their appearance in six months.

Gone was the immaculate dress uniform with the brass pips and polished Sam Brown; my father was now in battle dress which was badly crumpled and the hair showing beneath his cap had turned grey. He looked a lot older and

I noticed that as he fiddled with his pipe, his hands were shaking. My mother, who had always presented herself as if about to attend a garden party at Buckingham Palace, was also looking bedraggled. She had no hat on her head and her hair was in disarray and she was not even wearing lipstick. We learned later that they had had a nightmare journey through bombing and air raids, and that it had taken twice as long as expected.

A sudden squall sent us all scurrying inside the house where further greetings and introductions were carried out. Their two small cases were taken upstairs after my father had unpacked a bottle of scotch. We all squeezed into the parlour where Mrs Ladd and Megan served afternoon tea in front of a blazing fire. Rene and I sat on either side of our mother on the sofa. Our father was seated on the best chair next to the fire answering questions about the war from Mr Ladd and Benny, who wanted to know how he could become a spitfire pilot. Mrs Ladd was asking my mother about shortages and rationing. Rene and I just sat and listened, waiting for our turn; at least now all the conversation was in English.

After a couple of hours and a couple of whiskies our parents indicated they would like a short rest before changing for dinner, and taking some hot water with them they went to their bedroom. Conversation immediately reverted to Welsh as Rene and I sat with mixed emotions, deep in thought. We were both shocked by our parents appearance and decided not to worry them about our few hardships, such as our lack of clothing and our long walk to school. We had failed to notice that our appearance had changed too and our parents were also worried about our pale and skinny looks.

Our parents came down looking refreshed after their rest and change of clothes. Standing by the fire in the parlour before dinner the men discussed the state of the war, while Rene and I sat next to our mother giving positive answers to all her questions regarding our coping with the isolation and our basic amenities, while she gave us only reassuring replies to our questions about the war and our home and parental safety.

After all our excitement Rene and I felt tired and were quite happy to go to bed early that night, especially when our mother said she would come up and tuck us in. We were in heaven but we also realised that it would soon be time to say goodbye again, and as we lay in our bed we could hear the sounds of talking going on until sleep arrived.

I was up early Christmas morning and our parents were still resting when I went downstairs and found Mrs Ladd alone in the kitchen. She seemed quite excited to see me and asked if I knew what I was having for Christmas from my parents. I told her I had no idea but she offered to tell me saying she had been shown my present the night before, in secret. Rene and I had been told not to expect much because of the war time restrictions but Mrs Ladd seemed about to burst and had aroused my curiosity. I didn't want to spoil things for my parents by cheating but the decision was made for me when Mrs Ladd could no longer contain herself and told me it was a tractor, and with difficulty tried to explain to me what it looked like.

When we were all gathered together after breakfast to exchange presents my mother asked me what I would like as my present and after naming a few of my favourite toys I told her I really would like a tractor thinking to please her. She then asked me if I would like a train set but of course I said I wouldn't and that what I really would like was a tractor. She looked a little disappointed as she handed me a big box which I soon discovered contained a train set. As I glared at Mrs Ladd I almost called her a silly old cow, surely she new the difference between a train and a tractor. Of course, I realised later that she didn't, having had precious little to do with either in her lifetime. It was not uncommon in that part of Wales for the older generation never to have been on a train or seen a tractor. I couldn't tell my mother that Mrs Ladd had told me it was a tractor, all I could do was to say that I hadn't expected a train set in war time and I played with it non-stop till their departure.

Christmas day passed quickly and sitting down at the table laden with food it was hard to think about the war. Mrs Ladd had excelled herself and I forgave her for her stupidity. Our parents were very appreciative and fears about our welfare were dispelled when they saw us being well cared for by kind people. But they had only travelled by taxi from the village to the farm so they had not had to endure the uphill walk through a storm, neither had they had to endure, sitting for days and nights, listening to a strange language. Rene and I also told them we lacked nothing and that we were happy and did not want to be moved. So, it was with a sense of relief that they left the next day in the taxi which they had arrived in. Rene and I tried to hold back our tears as we stood with the Ladds and waved them good-bye, wondering where and when we would meet again.

It had hardly stopped raining during our parents' visit and this made trips outside to the toilet almost a guarantee for a cold shower. The rain also prevented us from going for walks which deprived our parents of the chance to see some of the most beautiful scenery in Wales. On the positive side, they were able to spend most of their time resting and relaxing in front of the fire, which they both needed. We learned later that our mother was involved in V.R.D. giving first aid to bomb victims, and because of my father's expertise in shipping all his postings were invariably to the docks, where the bombing was most heavy.

The period between our parents' departure and our return to school was a most depressing time for Rene and me. The toilet stood as a monument to their visit but was used less and less as the angle of its lean increased, causing the door to always stay open. The turkeys found out about this and commandeered the toilet for their dormitory until a storm blew it over, causing the stream to flood. Finally, it broke up distributing pieces of flotsam and jetsam along the banks of the stream.

Our first winter in Wales was unusually wet, and as the days grew shorter we spent more time inside the house which was cold and gloomy away from the fire. The routine of milking continued but the cows spent most of their time in the cowshed. The calves had all been sold and the dry cattle found shelter where they could. The ducks and geese enjoyed the flowing streams, but the chickens spent most of their time perching. The pigs opted to stay in their sties and were hand-fed and the horses lived in the stables which they left reluctantly when required to work, Turpin taking the milk to the truck then helping Prince pull the heavy plough guided by Benny, who was anxious to prepare the land for seeding in the early spring.

On wet and miserable days with little to occupy our minds, Rene and I would spend time indoors watching Mrs Ladd, who seemed to always be preparing meals. Although we realised that many things were now unobtainable because of the war, we doubted that the war made any difference to the food eaten at Dolrannog or any other farms around for that matter.

Apart from Sunday there was no variety in what we ate. Cawl was the staple diet. From the big black cauldron that lived on the stove vegetable soup was served at lunch and dinner. Mrs Ladd would chop up whatever vegetables were in season from the garden and in winter the choice would be small. Some meat, usually mutton, was added and allowed to simmer before potatoes and cabbage were added. After the evening bowl of soup the meat and vegetables were served, and the process was repeated the next day. The bottom of the big black pot was only ever seen in summer.

Sometimes when Rene and I were alone with Mrs Ladd she would talk to us about the war but she would often misunderstand what was happening as she did when she heard on the news that the Germans were gassing all the Jews and I asked her how they did it. In reply, she entered into great detail explaining how a gas pipe was inserted into the victim's body via the back passage, and the gas was turned on causing the body to inflate. The Germans would then turn the gas up until the pressure caused the body to float before bursting. She finished up by saying that this was mainly done to the women and children and would happen to all of us if the Germans invaded Wales.

Mrs Ladd would also tell us moralistic stories and here she would really let her imagination run riot, turning facts into fiction. One thing the stories had in common was that they all carried dire warnings of the consequences of indulging in the sins of the flesh. Unfortunately, they made little impact on me simply because I was too young to understand and Rene would not enlighten me as to their meanings.

One such yarn concerned a young man who had been sent away to work on a remote farm because of his uncontrollable desire for the company of bad women. It wasn't long before his obsession became so strong that he substituted the role played by the women with sheep. Becoming bored with this activity, he tried to satisfy his lust on a cow, but the cow's suction was too strong for him and the young man's body was reputedly found in the cowshed with his intestines spilled out on the floor.

Mrs Ladd also told us the story of a widow who lived in a cottage at the bottom of the valley. She warned us to stay away from her as she had a terrible disease which she had caught by going with too many men. She also told us that the smell of the widow was sickening, especially when the blow flies were around her in the summer because she didn't wash herself or keep the cottage clean.

Later on, when Mrs Ladd, Rene and I were out looking for some geese that had strayed, we met the widow at her front gate. Mrs Ladd was very friendly towards her and after a long conversation between the two we were invited in to taste her home made wines. Inside, the cottage was neat and tidy and like the widow herself was spotlessly clean. The wine, which the widow plied us with was cool and delicious, and barely alcoholic at all so she informed Mrs Ladd. The wines were made from all manner of fruit and vegetables and we were given sips from quite a few varieties, all of which Mrs Ladd seemed to enjoy.

We were all in a merry mood as we struggled up the steep side of the valley on our way home. I asked Mrs Ladd if the widow lady was completely cured now, but apparently she was too out of breath to answer. We had forgotten about the geese too.

Although the hours of daylight were short, the days seemed to drag and the evenings were worse. When the cows were left in the cowshed, Rene and I would help feed them while Benny put down clean straw for bedding before joining the rest of the family around the kitchen table for the evening meal. This was hastily consumed so that everyone could move to the fireside to listen to the news. Mr Ladd and Benny occupied the wooden settle, Mr Ladd next to the wireless with Benny closest to the fire, almost under the open chimney, where rain and lumps of soot would occasionally fall, causing the fire to sparkle.

Mrs Ladd and Megan sat opposite the men on the old couch, suffering the discomfort of misaligned springs which now held no resemblance to the manufacturer's design.

This left two places for Rene and me, one between Mrs Ladd and the fire and the other next to Megan, furthermost from the fire, which gave us the choice of cooking on one side or freezing on the other since most of the heat from the fire went straight up the chimney. This resulted in Rene and me continually changing places. This, at times caused friction as we would both have to be suffering the same degree of discomfort before an agreement to move was made.

At seven o'clock sharp we were told to stop fidgeting and be quiet when the radio was turned on and they all became engrossed with whatever the news reader was saying about the war. We could only guess what was happening by their exclamations and facial expressions, having to wait until the news was over and the radio switched off before someone, usually Megan, gave us any form of translation.

This routine was played out every night and it was the only time the wireless was turned on, the accumulator having to be taken to the village for charging.

So, it was with mixed feeling that we went back to school. We were glad to get out of the house but the winter of 1940 was very wet, and there were few days that we made the journey with our clothes still dry. Rene seemed to have settled down and enjoyed being at school with Miss Foy whom she admired so much. Although we all thought Miss Foy old, she was probably only a little over forty. She was short and roundish with wispy hair and wore glasses. All the children, especially her senior class, came to love her, yet everyone respected her also.

Not only did she bring about order from chaos which enabled the children to obtain some standard of education, she also managed to sort out the children's social problems with the locals. Not all the billeting arrangements were satisfactory to begin with. Some of the boys were undisciplined and caused problems in their foster homes.

Other children, especially the younger ones, were desperately homesick. Some children's family members became war casualties and some just lost contact.

Miss Foy did her best to keep the children happy. The war was not discussed and the younger children spent a lot of time being read to by their teacher or doing some other quiet occupation like drawing or writing. This enabled Miss Foy to teach the senior class a comprehensive syllabus without distraction. However, if we became bored with our lesson there was nothing to stop us from listening to what Miss Foy was saying.

To keep her class fully occupied Miss Foy always had some extra-curricular activity in progress and as time passed these became more ambitious, culminating in a stage production of the Pirates of Penzance. It hadn't taken Miss Foy long to correctly recognise Rene as having above average intelligence but also lacking in self confidence as a result of her mental breakdown. This had been caused by swotting, under pressure from our mother, to attain a scholarship to college. Miss Foy and Rene developed a very close relationship which gave Rene the courage to accept the part of the nurse.

I found it hard to concentrate in school and became bored and learned little. I also found it hard to form a real friendship with anyone because living so far from the village prevented me from joining in any of the after school activities with the other boys.

Although it didn't snow often the wind blew very cold and our fingers and toes became very painful as we both developed chilblains. Rene and I started to miss days from school, a fact which did not go unnoticed by Miss Foy,

164

which caused more worry to Rene than me.

Other teachers came and went but Miss Foy, not only stayed for the duration, but made her home in the village after the war, opening a tea room in the village square before retiring to her cottage. Not only was she accepted by the local population but was also highly respected.

Above the clouds, although not noticeable at first, the sun was spending a little more time in the sky each day, and as the first term of the year came to an end we realised that we had survived our first winter on the mountain. Spring was in the air.

Chapter 14

MECHANISATION

Romance was in the air too. Wynfred married Megan and took her from Dolrannog to Gronllwyn, his farm six miles further up the valley. It was a quiet war-time wedding, which took place at the chapel that Wynfred belonged to. No long white dress, just a sensible tailored costume for the bride and a suit for the groom. We did not attend but went to school as usual. We were happy for Megan but knew we would miss her. She had been a tower of strength for Rene and I wondered how my sister would cope. I needn't have worried for soon after the wedding we had another surprise, Emrys had bought Pen-rhiw, the farm next door, which meant that Mona and Rene could spend more time together.

On moving day, the procession made up of all of Emrys's worldly goods would not have presented any threat to a Barnham and Bailey circus parade, but it did have certain similarities. Mair led the way on top of a cart piled high with furniture, grasping the reins with one hand and holding the baby, Tegwyn, to her with the other. Mona followed, giving a great performance as an animal trainer, because the cow she was leading had no desire to move to a new home and was resolutely trying to return to her old one.

Next, followed Tom Selby on a cart, also piled high. He was a relative of the family and was lending a hand before moving into Waun Uchaf himself. Balanced on top of his cart was a roughly made cage of wire which held all the poultry. Unfortunately, the largest of the cockerels was also very much against moving to a new home and had succeeded in getting half his body out through the wire, the half with the sharp bits with which he was now attacking Tom. Tom, who was in much pain and performing like a contortionist was valiantly trying to thwart the bird's escape.

Now circuses always have an act comprising a clown and a funny car and this act was epitomised by Emrys himself as he came into view trying to master the controls of a most dilapidated Austin Seven. He kept well to the rear of the procession so as not to upset the animals even more, since the car would, without warning, backfire and send a cloud of smoke out of its exhaust pipe. The back of the car was also piled high and on the front seat the heavy milk separator had been squeezed in, which unfortunately caused the passenger door to fly open. This caused Emrys to hastily lean across to close it. This resulted in his inadvertently turning the wheel and causing the car to swerve.

As the parade passed through Dolrannog the participants carried on a shouting conversation with Mrs Ladd who was watching from the front porch. On hearing the noise of the car Benny had also arrived on the scene just as the engine stalled and so allowed him a closer look.

Benny lost no time in making scathing remarks to Emrys about the car pointing out that its canvas roof was rotten, the side curtains non-existent and that the wire wheels were rusty and wobbled as their tyres were worn and flat. He finished by saying that it looked more like a dilapidated old pram than a car.

Emrys hopped out wearing only his left clog, explaining that he could not operate the tiny brake pedal or the accelerator separately when wearing the right clog too. Then grasping the crank handle, arm muscles bulging, he spun it with such gusto that the little car bounced up and down on its springs. This caused the passenger door to fly open once again which inspired Emrys to make a leap that any Cossack dancer would have been proud of as he managed to close it before the separator fell to the ground. Grinning from ear to ear he squeezed behind the wheel again and with a crunch of gears and a wave of his hand he set off to catch up with the others. Benny was jealous and watched with envy as Emrys disappeared in a cloud of exhaust smoke. Pen-rhiw had mechanised transport before Dolrannog, but more was to come.

During the first few days of settling in, the baby Austin made several trips between the two farms and Benny and Emrys spent much time with their heads under the bonnet, blowing through the fuel lines and cleaning the carburettor. A small screwdriver and spanner and a large darning needle seemed to suffice as a tool kit capable of keeping the car going. Stopping was another problem and was mainly achieved by switching the ignition off and letting the car roll to a halt.

Feeling more confident, Emrys decided it was time to

take the car for a longer run and a visit to Megan was decided on. Mrs Ladd refused point blank to go anywhere near the car, Mr Ladd declined politely, and Benny, whose pride had been hurt, could in no way condescend to ride as a passenger in a car driven and owned by Emrys. When Rene and I were asked I eagerly accepted and after gaining assurance that Mona was definitely coming too, Rene agreed.

The following Saturday was fine as we climbed into the back seat with Mona. Mair was sitting in the front, next to Emrys, nursing baby Tegwyn as we made a cautious start down the lane. I couldn't help thinking of our first ride in the Austin Seven owned by the minister when he drove us to Dolrannog on our first night in Wales, though there was no comparison between the two models. One was neat and black and the other so dilapidated, but at least we were moving. At first all went well. We were on a steady run down the mountainside to Ty'n Rhos where we joined the narrow bitumen road that would take us along the bottom of the valley. It was quite flat, though the road twisted over narrow stone bridges as it changed from one side of the river to the other. There was no room for two vehicles to pass, but since we saw not another soul the problem was purely academic.

After about five miles we had to branch off and take a road that climbed steeply up the side of the valley right to the top, then through the little village of Llanychâr after which we would soon be at Megan's.

We had to approach the hill from a sharp bend, so we were not travelling very fast as we started the climb and Emrys had to change gear as the little engine started to labour. We were less than half way up when another gear change was needed. Doubt as to the laden car's ability to climb the hill now crept into all our minds, and I could see the knuckles of Emrys's hands shining white as he gripped the little steering wheel tightly. The final gear change was made on full throttle, producing a screech of protest from the gearbox. Amazingly, the engine kept its revs up but couldn't transmit the power to the back wheels as the clutch had started to slip and was now producing a blue smoky haze.

Forward momentum finally ceased about two thirds up the side of the valley when the engine died, sending up little puffs of steam and Emrys now had his big foot firmly planted on the brake pedal. Inevitably, we started to roll backwards as the brakes lost their effectiveness. Emrys now yanked the hand brake on with such force that it came away in his hand. He promptly discarded the same by throwing it over the side and I watched in horror as it fell to the floor of the valley hundreds of feet below.

Now Emrys had only just learned to drive and although he could manage to steer a car forward, reversing was a skill he had not yet acquired. It soon became obvious that we were not going to stay on the narrow road all the way back down and as the speed increased so did Emrys's turns of the steering wheel which caused the car to zigzag across the road. There was only two feet clearance on either side so it would not be long before we either crashed into the bank or went over the edge.

At this point Mair screamed something to Emrys who then, more by luck than judgement, managed to steer the car against the bank. For one horrible moment it seemed we would bounce off the bank and over the edge but Emrys managed to hold the wheel over and finally the car came to a scraping stop. Unharmed, we all climbed out but we couldn't stop shaking and even Emrys's sun-tanned face had taken on a sickly hue.

The car was not badly damaged and a few more dents and scratches would hardly be noticed. The back mudguard was jammed against its wheel but a good yank from Emrys soon fixed that.

The little engine soon cooled down and after some vigorous turning of the crank handle Emrys succeeded in bringing it back to life, but was unable to get the car moving as the clutch continued to slip. Mair would not let go of the baby but the rest of us pushed and eventually got the car onto some level ground at the top of the hill where Emrys was able to get in and drive it.

We were less than two miles from Megan's farm and we all flatly refused to accompany Emrys, preferring to walk in safety and leave him to drive on his own. As it turned out we all arrived at about the same time as Emrys had to reverse the car up a couple of hills which fortunately had no obstacles to worry him.

After the ritual of morning tea for which Megan had cooked fresh Welsh cakes and pancakes, I followed Wynfred and Emrys outside. What a contrast they made! Emrys was thick set and weather beaten, his hands were tough and his nails uneven and unclean, his clothes were baggy and he wore an old greasy trilby hat on his head; he was and looked a man of the land. Wynfred was immaculate and looked more like a music teacher than a farmer. His clothes were neat and tidy covered by a dust coat, his slim white hands and fingernails perfectly clean and, a pale thin face with glasses peered from under a tweed cap.

The farm reflected Wynfred's neatness, everything was kept clean and tidy and there was no doubt that a lot of work had gone into the running of the farm since before his marriage, Wynfred had lived alone and had only one farm hand to help him.

The cowshed accommodated thirty six milking cows, all black and white, a pure Friesian herd. These were milked morning and night every day of the year but, like everything else on the farm, it was done by machine. In the implement shed was a tractor with rubber tyres and although it was several years old it still looked brand new, as did all the other machines. A workshop in the corner had every tool in its proper place with not a bit of rust to be seen. Even the pig pens which contained over twenty pigs, smelt sweetly of fresh straw. The hay was stacked in bales in a huge shed and other feed was neatly stacked away in a big barn, but what caught Emrys's attention was Wynfred's immaculate Morris Eight sedan, black paint shining and in its own garage.

Back inside the house all the females were looking at Megan's new stove, a huge Aga cooker not black but finished in cream enamel, with a polished steel hotplate. Megan had the house looking like a new pin, and compared with Dolrannog it was much larger and looked quite modern.

After lunch we walked through the fields where all the fences were in good repair and all the gates opened and shut at the touch of a finger. From what we saw Gronllwyn must have been at least twice as big as Dolrannog.

The men spent about an hour on the Austin Seven after which Wynfred declared he would drive us home in his car, although Emrys insisted that he would drive himself back. Megan decided to come with us for the ride which caused us all to be squashed in, with me sitting in the front on Megan's lap, which I didn't mind at all. The little car, although grossly overloaded, purred along without any fuss under Wynfred's most capable driving and we felt sad when it was time for Megan to leave us again, although we could not but feel happy that she had found such a kind man for a husband. That night in our bed Rene and I couldn't help but wonder why the two farms were so different.

One morning, shortly after our trip to see Megan, Mair and Emrys passed by in the pony and float. Benny was just in time to pass some remark about having a car but still using real horse power as, with a big grin on his face, Emrys broke the horse into a trot and quickly disappeared around the bend without replying.

It became more of a mystery when about an hour later Mair returned in the float on her own. All she would say was Emrys was coming later. Thinking no more about it, everyone went back to their jobs until disturbed by a strange sound; something was approaching Dolrannog. The noise grew louder and Emrys appeared around the bend seated on the oldest tractor imaginable.

It was brownish in colour but not from paint; it was completely covered in rust. Its wheels were made of iron and the back ones had steel lugs on them which caused them to clatter as they travelled over the stony surface. Its exhaust pipe went straight up in the air devoid of a silencer, so the noise of the engine was deafening.

Just as it reached the gate the tractor backfired and stopped dead and Emrys climbed down from its metal seat just as everyone gathered around. It was giving out a lot of heat and making ominous hissing and ticking sounds.

Benny wanted to know if Emrys had gone into the scrap metal business. But Emrys had decided that if he was to become a proper farmer rather than a trapper, he was at least going to be mechanised like Wynfred. Benny mentioned something about a bloody junk yard.

After an hour even Emrys gave up trying to start the tractor, but it couldn't remain blocking the gateway to Dolrannog so Benny harnessed up Prince, who looked warily at the machine which he was chained to. With Benny at Prince's head the procession moved to Pen-rhiw where the tractor was left just inside the front gate where it was to remain forever. After a few death defying trips down the mountain and a warning from the local constabulary, the Austin Seven also came to rest alongside the house.

But Emrys could now enjoy having the last word when he and Benny were having an argument about farming. It gave him great pleasure to point out that Pendre was a far more mechanised farm than Dolrannog even though some of the machinery needed maintenance at that particular time.

Chapter 15

SPRING

After the long wet winter the Springtime was most welcome and to none more so than Lil, Dolrannog's Welsh sheep dog, because from now until the end of summer she would be kept busy doing her job of working the sheep. The sheep had been left undisturbed to fend for themselves on the open mountain since late autumn. All the farms that bordered this vast rocky terrain grazed their sheep there for most of the year, their flock number being in ratio to the acreage of their farms. Some of the bigger farms could have flocks of thousands and the small ones like Dolrannog, just a few hundred.

The Welsh mountain sheep are a hardy breed; not many other breeds could survive the harsh winter on a mountainside. Not noted for its wool, which is often black and seldom cuts more than five pounds even from a wether, its meat is most sought after and Welsh lamb is about the best meat a butcher can offer.

Fortunately this breed tends to be territorial and does not wander far from home and seldom do the flocks become mixed up. The odd few that do get lost or wander are soon recognised by their markings and returned to their rightful owners.

The rams had been running with the flocks since late October and theoretically, by now, all the ewes should be pregnant. It was time to bring them down from the mountain to the protection of the walled fields below for them to drop their lambs. Rough shelters had been built across the corners of the dry stone walls giving some protection from frost or a late fall of snow. Foxes and birds of prey were also an ever present threat to a weakened ewe or a new born lamb. Although it was rarely needed, assistance was available in the case of a difficult birth and extra feed was at hand if required, though the mountain sheep tended only to eat its natural food.

Benny led his team up the mountain, Lil at his heels with her tail and ears pointing straight up to the sky. Next to him and talking in his usual machine gun-like chatter was Emrys with his dog closely in attendance. Mair, who had left baby Tegwyn with Mrs Ladd, was next in line with Tom Selby, who was now installed with his family at Waun Uchaf and had also bought his dog along. Rene and Mona followed and Mr Ladd and I brought up the rear. I always liked being with Mr Ladd and thought of him as the grandfather I never had. He was the one who took the time to explain to me about farming and answer all my questions with patience. I thought Mr Ladd was a very wise and scholarly man, his writing being in the most beautiful copper plate style. His philosophy on life was simple and he told me to always act honestly and to have faith in God, and by doing so I would always be rewarded. I couldn't help thinking of the hard life Mr Ladd endured trying to make a living from Dolrannog and suspected that his reward would not be of this world.

The climb was not too arduous and we made good time with a fresh breeze off the ocean keeping us comfortable. Unusually the sky was a deep blue and completely devoid of cloud. This was certainly to our advantage, giving us good visibility, and enabling anyone as experienced as Benny to spot a stray sheep a mile away. Trying to drive sheep off the mountain when visibility was poor, through mist or rain, was almost impossible with even the best sheep dogs to help.

We fanned out under Benny's orders and began a three mile sweep up and across the mountain before swinging in a giant arc back down to the fence line, driving the ever increasing flock of sheep before us. It was all done in an orderly fashion and when Benny did spot a stray Dolrannog sheep a mile away, I would watch in fascination as, on his command, Lil would race off towards the stray ewe but slow to a walk on approach and quietly return it to the flock.

With due consideration of the pregnant ewes, the flock was moved slowly down through a couple of fields to the farm yard where the gates were all secured and the dogs left on guard while everyone went inside and demolished the food Mrs Ladd had prepared. We were all tired and hungry having walked many miles and breakfast seemed a long time ago, but there was more to do yet.

Outside with the sheep again it was the half a dozen rams that were first separated from the flock. Easily distinguishable by their long curly horns they were temporarily shut in the stable, while the ewes and the wethers were separated. The drafting was carried out by

Benny. A temporary race restricted the sheep, forcing them forward in single file. A swing gate at the end of it divided the sheep as Benny, grasping its handle, moved it from side to side, wethers to the left, ewes to the right. This process was facilitated by the different ear markings on the sheep. The wethers were then allowed to wander back up the mountain and the ewes put into their prepared quarters.

As the farm yard emptied, Mr Ladd, Lil and I drove the rams to their special paddock which had extra strong fences. Mr Ladd explained to me they might need some new rams for next year to keep a good blood line in the flock, and roughly only one ram was needed for each fifty ewes. In the meantime their celibate state was confirmed by the high fence.

On our return a gory sight greeted us in the ewes' paddock. A young ewe had given birth to a premature lamb which was dead and an old ewe had given birth to twins which, though small, were alive. Premature twins are hard to rear, so Benny had introduced one of them to the young ewe. To encourage the adoption he had first rubbed the lamb in the blood from under the tail of the young ewe, who was now suspiciously sniffing the lamb as it lay on the ground. Sensing a warm udder close by, the lamb struggled to its feet and we would have cheered, but for frightening the sheep, as the ewe started licking the lamb as it staggered towards a teat which it was allowed to suck. Rene and I could have stayed and watched all day but were told that this would upset the ewes and we were sent to fetch the cows as the milking and other chores still had to be done. It was getting late and we were tired and very glad that we didn't have to milk as well after the long hard day.

Next morning, Mr Ladd thanked us for our help, telling us that we had done a good job. Apparently, they were happy with the sheep numbers. Some losses were to be expected especially amongst the older sheep since foxes and birds of prey attacked anything that had become weak. Although useful in cleaning up the afterbirth thus keeping the blowflies down, crows would attack a new born lamb sometimes pecking out its eyes and foxes would bite off a lamb's head leaving the body behind on the ground; another reason for bringing the ewes down from the mountain.

From then on every morning before school we checked to see how many lambs had been born and again when we arrived home. The ewes were a mixed lot. Some of the younger ones had trouble with their first lamb and needed help usually from Benny or Mr Ladd. Some of the older ewes proved to be barren and were later sold as mutton.

Inevitably, we finished up with orphans who for some reason or other had been rejected by their mother or whose mother had died giving birth. Lambs who were sick or deformed were quickly disposed of but, in all, Rene and I were allowed to bottle feed about six pet lambs morning and night. Pet lambs were generally regarded as a nuisance in the flock became they grew up without fear of man or dog, so their lives were generally rather short, since they were the first to appear on the dinner table or wrapped in bread as a cold meat sandwich. The luckier ones were sold.

Spring saw a marked improvement in the weather. Torrential rain and gales gave way to showers and soft breezes and each day, the sun tried to warm the earth for a little longer. It made our jobs more pleasant, though we were never expected to work outside in heavy weather or give much help on school days. At weekends and during school holidays however, we joined in the work like any other farm children.

The fetching of cows for milking and then returning them to their pastures was the easiest of jobs if the weather was fine and I often did this on my own. It could become frustrating though if a rain squall threatened when the cows were in the confines of the narrow lane. There was no way of hurrying them as they waddled along, their udders full and swinging, making their own leisurely pace to the cow shed and completely ignoring my shouts and the barking of the dogs. Indeed, Mrs Ladd told me not to hurry the cows as the milk in their udders would turn to butter and kill them. Nobody else seemed to know about that though! If it rained before the cows entered the yard, it just meant one more soaking for me and it worried the cows not at all.

Spring brought about one magic surprise for Rene and me, which helped relieve the monotony for a while. After a heavy fall of rain we experienced a few days of warm weather and now, all the fields were wearing their new green covers. We were waiting at the gate for the last of the cows to leave when Rene called my attention to what appeared to be a mass of large white pebbles strewn across the grass. We certainly had not noticed them before and on closer examination they proved to be mushrooms, hundreds of mushrooms, some bigger than saucers. Apart from a few damaged by the cows treading on them, they were all perfect, snow-white on top and dusty pink underneath. We picked one and smelt it before peeling it and then tentatively tasting it, instantly experiencing its unique earthy flavour.

We were not too familiar with mushrooms and only ever had them as a treat, so we decided to take a couple back to the farmhouse to show Mrs Ladd. She told us it was the right time for mushrooms and indeed they were proper ones. She also told us that they only ever grew in that particular field and did not appear every year. After we had fed the calves, Mrs Ladd handed us a large wicker basket and we waited impatiently for milking to finish. Eventually we followed the cows to their field and in less than five minutes had filled the basket to overflowing with the biggest of the mushrooms but on looking back after shutting the gate, there seemed to be even more of them than before.

Back at the house Mrs Ladd's eyes nearly popped out as we set the overflowing basket on the table. We helped prepare the mushrooms by peeling them and discarding the stalks. Meanwhile, the heavy iron frying pan had been put on the stove with a generous dob of butter and a little water in it, to which the mushrooms were added and allowed to cook away. When the liquid had turned to a creamy consistency the mushrooms had turned black and were ready to serve. Fresh bread was cut and buttered and the bowls filled with generous helpings as everyone sat around the table to feast on the first crop of mushrooms. The bowls were wiped clean with the crust of the loaf, except by Mr Ladd who had to use bread as he could not bite properly with his loose teeth.

During the next two weeks, we had mushrooms with everything, but Rene and I were the only ones who bothered to pick them and eventually even that became boring. We would make a game of it by trying to pick a basketful of perfect, large mushrooms without letting our feet move off the cow trail, or we would allow ourselves only to pick so many from each ring, for the mushrooms grew in rings. Mrs Ladd said they were fairy rings but Mr Ladd said the rings were formed by the warming of the ground by a cow lying down to sleep at night.

The mushrooms finished as abruptly as they had started, much to everyone's relief; enough is enough. For every one we had picked we must have left behind a hundred. Thousands of mushrooms must have been left to rot in that short season. Rene and I could not understand why they were not harvested and sold. The people of London had to queue just for their basic rations.

Apart from being the busiest time of the year for the farm, Spring was also a time of hope and expectation as the harsh winter weather gave way to more sunny days. The fruits of Benny's hard labour were now becoming apparent as green shoots appeared in the fields that he had persisted in ploughing, regardless of the weather. A sack thrown over his head and shoulders for extra protection was the only concession he made to the weather if the rain turned to sleet or hail. The horses, having to work harder sent up clouds of steam from their hot breath.

I never tired of watching Benny work the horses. Ploughing was hard on man and beast and I could only admire the way he guided the heavy single furrow plough around the larger rocks yet managed to keep each row straight.

I was more intrigued when the time to plant the seed

came and Benny would march up and down the rows with the precision of a guardsman on parade. The seed was scattered with the aid of a simple hand-operated machine called a broadcaster, commonly known as a fiddle as it was operated with a bow. It was this that had caught my attention in the ceiling rack when I first stood in the kitchen at Dolrannog.

The seed was carried in a sack like container slung over one shoulder, and this had a metal tube protruding from a bottom corner which, when held in one hand, could be swivelled in any direction. The seed was forced out of the tube by an impeller mounted on a spindle. In the opposite hand the bow was held, the string of which had been wound around the spindle a couple of times. Pushing and pulling on the bow caused the spindle to spin quickly back ond forth thus scattering or broadcasting the seed in a fine spray.

Good concentration was required if an even spreading of the seed was to be achieved and Benny took care to walk up and down the rows with a measured step synchronised with the strokes of the bow on the fiddle. To keep his rhythm he would break into a Welsh marching song. It was indeed a sight to behold when Benny was in full swing with seed spraying out of the fiddle in time with the 'Men of Harlech' sung at the top of his voice. When he had finished there would not be another breath left in Benny and sweat would be pouring off him, even on a cool day.

There were very few easy jobs at Dolrannog.

A late frost was an ever-threatening disaster at this time of the year, not only could it cause serious loss among the baby lambs but also to the crops. I would follow Benny as he inspected the green shoots of the new season's crops, all standing in perfectly straight rows and standing erect like soldiers on parade. He cast a critical eye over the delicate green carpet before allowing a look of satisfaction to appear on his face and, with justifiable pride, he would point out to me the various crops so neatly arranged.

Dew drops were still hanging from the tips of the long grass in the hay field which was lush and green and the warmth of the sun gave it a smell of sweetness. It would soon be ready for cutting, then drying before stacking. We passed on to look at the potato crop and here Benny stopped and lit a cigarette as a look of disappointment came over his face.

To my eyes the plants looked dark green and healthy with little white flowers growing in abundance. Like all the other crops they stood in perfectly straight rows, with each plant equidistant from its neighbour and rightly so as a measuring stick had been used to indicate where each seed potato had to be placed, Rene and I had joined everyone else at the planting.

The potato crop was very important to Dolrannog and its position had been carefully chosen and well fertilised because Dolrannog not only grew potatoes for domestic use, but also as one of the main cash crops.

Now, watching Benny, I remembered the argument he had had with his father at the time of planting. There was always a friendly rivalry between the farmers as to who had the biggest bull or whose lambs fetched the best price or who had the neatest haystacks and Benny liked to have, or be, the best. But the strongest rivalry, however, was to see who brought the first of the new season's potatoes to market and that farmer would be rewarded with the highest price for his crop. The only way to be first was to plant the seed potatoes before anyone else, but the earlier this was done so the risk of damage from frost increased. It was not uncommon for some of the farms to lose part of their crop and indeed some finished up with no crop at all.

The fact of the matter was that Dolrannog could not afford to gamble. It needed a good potato crop and Mr Ladd, being a conservative type of person, would not give in to Benny's urgings to plant earlier and his frustration showed as he kicked away some of the earth around a potato plant and, bending down, scraped out a few small potatoes. There was no chance of Dolrannog being first to market this season and turning to me he swore that one day he would have his own farm with a tractor and a car and then he would show the locals how to grow early potatoes. And of course, being Benny, he did, in time do just that.

Weeks later when the leaves had withered and the flowers died it was time to lift the potatoes. Everyone from Dolrannog, Pendre and Waun Uchaf gathered together as they would all share in the harvest. Firstly, with Prince harnessed to a potato lifter, a machine very similar to a plough, Benny steered the single prong deep down the middle of each row to spew potatoes onto the surface.

The younger ones would collect these in buckets and take them to where Turpin was standing with the float loaded with empty sacks. Here they were roughly graded, the perfect ones brushed and bagged for market, misshapen or damaged ones put into other bags for domestic use and undersized ones put separately into another bag.

After Benny had finished furrowing the men went back over the ground with forks and mattocks to make sure that no potatoes were left behind. It was back breaking work eased only by the singing and humour as someone would cry out holding aloft an extra large specimen or a potato that had grown into a grotesque shape and prompting ribald remarks which Mr Ladd unsuccessfully tried to curtail. I picked up a potato that closely resembled a round fat lady and was about to hold it up to show Mrs Ladd when an icy look from Rene caused me to change my mind.

We were tired at the end of the afternoon when we left the men to cart the potatoes into the barn. As usual, we fetched the cows for milking and while this was going on we fed the calves whose numbers were on the increase. Later, after we had returned the cows to their field we entered the farm house where everyone was gathered to celebrate the completion of a productive potato harvest, Mrs Ladd had been working hard as usual and in addition to all the other dishes on the table she produced two large bowls of fresh baby potatoes smothered with fresh farm butter. As usual when there was a gathering someone started singing and everyone joined in, but with bulging stomach I was happy to climb the stairs to bed. After a shortened version of my prayers and telling God I would make up for it next time, I fell asleep with the choir below singing 'All Through the Night'.

We were glad that the next day was Sunday for the only work done on the Sabbath was the milking of the cows. As usual, we joined Mr Ladd for the walk to chapel. Mrs Ladd was excused because of her sore feet, but we were surprised when Benny joined us as he had usually gone flying down the mountain on his push bike by this time of the day. Mr Ladd and Benny led the way talking quietly to each other. Rene and I followed in silence, deep in our own thoughts.

I was thinking of home and our walk to Sunday school through a maze of streets whose cement footpaths gave access to the rows of identical brick houses, all trying to hide behind the smoke that wafted from their identical chimneys. Although our mother professed to being Church of England we only attended as a family twice a year, at Christmas and Easter, but it was she who had firmly expressed the wish that we keep up our religious observances. At the time she could have had no idea of the walking distance involved.

Although there was a church in the village where the service was conducted in English, we chose to attend the chapel. Firstly because most of the walk although of a similar distance was not the way we walked to school, and gave us some variation, and secondly because we knew how boring a church service was compared to one held in a Welsh chapel.

We were now no longer fussed over on our arrival but were accepted as part of the scene. Indeed, people often spoke to us in Welsh, forgetting we could only speak English. Inside the chapel we enjoyed the enthusiasm of the congregation as they sang their songs of praise. Rene and I, after hearing the same hymns sung repeatedly, were able to join in parrot fashion, not knowing the meaning of the words. We even found the sermon entertaining as we watched the antics of the preacher as he delivered it in his rhetorical way, shouting and raising his arms in the air and stirring the congregation to reply with loud 'Hallelujahs'.

On our way back up the mountain to Dolrannog we were surprised when Mr Ladd broke into English after having been in conversation with Benny. It became obvious that he and Benny had been discussing the potato crop and now he addressed us all in his quiet way. He pointed out the foolishness of gambling and taking unnecessary risks just for the sake of pride. He also said that by being cautious they had avoided the danger of loss from frost and had been successful in growing a healthy and profitable crop. Their reward would be only a little less than what the farmer received for his early crop and this they had achieved with much less worry. Mr Ladd concluded by quoting from the Bible that the Lord should not be tempted, but thanked for all his mercy.

At this point I was getting hot and tired and the only thing I felt thankful to God for was the fact that it was only three miles from the chapel to Dolrannog, and not four, since one of my shoes was once again coming apart.

Springtime was busy for Mrs Ladd too, especially now that Megan was not at home. Mona had her own work to do at Pen-rhiw but came over whenever she could. Rene and I were at school more now as the weather improved but also helped when we could. As cows were calving again, we resumed our chore of getting the calves' formula at night, and fetching and taking back the milking cows, who no longer needed to be fed hay.

The vegetable garden became a hive of activity. It was situated at the opposite end of the house to the farmyard and was enclosed by a higher than usual stone wall which also had chicken wire on the top. Even so, the odd chicken or rabbit managed to get in. The garden was protected from the wind and with the soil enriched over the years with unlimited manure and fertiliser, to me it seemed part of a different world. At times it was almost tropical and was always warmer and quieter. There would always be something green and growing even in winter, and this plot provided all the vegetables and fruit for use all year round. The men did the hard work of digging and spreading the manure, but it was all hands on deck to help Mrs Ladd plant and weed at the appropriate times. As we became familiar with the garden we were often asked to cut a cabbage or pull some carrots to put in the *cawl*.

Apart from every known vegetable, the garden also produced cane fruits like raspberries, loganberries and gooseberries in which I developed a keen interest. On one occasion when Rene and I were in the garden helping Mrs Ladd I just happened to notice that the gooseberry bush had some large ripe gooseberries on it ready for picking. Mrs Ladd was intent on her weeding and didn't notice my disappearance, as I stuffed my mouth full and returned to the patch I was meant to be weeding. Rene and Mrs Ladd were chatting away so I decided on seconds, but this time I took a little longer for my selection as I became aware that there were not as many really ripe gooseberries as I had first thought. While I was about it I also decided to put some emergency rations in my pocket. Again I returned undetected to my spot.

The weeding was boring and it wasn't long before my emergency rations were used up. I was feeling quite satisfied though until Mrs Ladd moved, turning her back to me and making me decide on one last sortie. As I glanced back at the bush I had to admit that it did look rather bare of ripe fruit, but I was not worried as there were still plenty of green ones left to ripen.

Soon Mrs Ladd came stiffly to her feet and declared that we had done enough for one day, saying also that she would bake us a gooseberry pie for a treat. She added that she had noticed just enough ripe ones on the bush, ready for picking. I could feel my cheeks burning as she searched the bush for ripe berries while Rene was giving me a funny look. Mrs Ladd was standing, hands on hips, staring at the denuded bush with a puzzled look on her face. I suggested that a flock of birds could be responsible then I felt a sudden pain in my stomach and quickly made a second suggestion that I should go and get the cows for milking and without waiting for a reply I beat a hasty retreat. When we finally sat down to apple pie again I was personally happy that it was not a gooseberry one as I felt my stomach twinge just at the thought of it.

It was time to spring clean the house and Mair and Mona spent several days helping Mrs Ladd, and for once I was quite happy to go to school. The big brass tub was brought in from the farmyard and all the sheets and covers from the beds were brought downstairs to be washed and the quilts were hung on the line and aired in the sun. All the doors and windows were left open and the cobwebs removed from the corners. All the china was removed from the dresser in the parlour and the one in the kitchen to allow the shelves to be dusted. All the wooden furniture was polished. The few rugs from the parlour and bedrooms were given a good beating outside.

We arrived home from school on a Friday afternoon just

in time to witness the final act, as the work had to be completed before the weekend. The flagstones, which extended through all the downstairs, were still damp from the scrubbing they had just received and we found Mona kneeling on the floor of the kitchen next to a pile of dandelion leaves. We watched in fascination as she tightly rolled some of the leaves into a cigar shape between her hands, and using this as a crude brush she vigorously rubbed a flagstone causing part of it to turn from red to green. This she must have been doing for some time for now all of the kitchen floor was covered in a perfect red and green geometric pattern, almost giving the effect of a lino-covered floor. It must have taken her hours, and was undoubtedly a back breaking task, but she finished it with pride. Looking at the floor, I noticed that the flagstones were worn in an uneven fashion by the clog irons where people had walked over the years.

The pattern lasted through the summer and was faintly visible for much longer, but I couldn't help wondering if it really was worth all that effort.

Chapter 16

SHEEP

The lambing season was over before the first day of summer and it was time for the lambs and the ewes to be sent back up the mountain. The warmer weather had brought about rapid growth to all living things and the abundant supply of lush green grass had seen the ewes quickly recuperate after lambing. It also guaranteed a plentiful supply of milk for the lambs. The lambs grew quickly and seemed to have an endless energy spending most of their days frolicking with their peers and the rest of the time feeding or sleeping. But this idyllic lifestyle was about to change in a cruel way, because before returning to the mountain the lambs had to be marked.

Once again the ewes and the lambs were gathered into the farmyard where they were drafted; the ewes separated from their lambs who were held in a temporary pen. This was no easy task as the lambs were very quick and objected strongly to being taken from their mothers. The noise was overwhelming as the lambs and the ewes called to each other continuously.

Once again Benny oversaw the operation and the two wooden benches were brought out from the back room of the house and placed longways pointing to the lamb pen. Mair and Mona each sat astride one, facing Tom Selby who was once again helping out. He was already in the lamb pen. Being nimble and quick on his feet he had been allocated the job as catcher. He would catch a lamb in each hand and pass them over the fence, one to Emrys and one to Benny, who would then sit the lamb on its bottom on the bench. Mair or Mona would grip the lamb tightly by its front legs and facing the man with the knife. He would then make several cuts on either the left or right ear depending on the lamb's sex, and this mark would also signify that it belonged to Dolrannog. Then the loose skin was pulled up the lamb's tail and a cut made between the two particular vertebrae to sever the tail. If it was a ewe lamb then the cutting was over, having taken only a few seconds, but if it happened to be a male it still had to endure the cruellest cut of all. Its testicles were squeezed down into the scrotum which was sliced open to reveal the testicles which after cutting the cords were removed. Sometimes the men had difficulty in grasping the testicles so then they would bite them off with their teeth and spit them out onto the ever-growing pile.

The dogs, who had been ordered to lie down, watched the proceedings with slavering mouths.

After the operation the bleeding lamb was placed on the ground where it remained shivering in shock and pain before slowly and stiffly walking away to find its mother.

I took a look at Rene who already had tears in her eyes as she turned away. I was sickened by the blood also, so I jumped into the pen to help Tom Selby catch the lambs and where I didn't have to watch the men with their knives.

When one of our pet lambs came up to me, I noticed as I passed it to Benny that it was a male and knew instantly how Judas Iscariot must have felt in the Garden of Gethsemane. Only the six of the best male lambs escaped castration following lengthy judgements regarding their suitability as breeding stock. These were allowed to grow into rams when they would be used for servicing the ewes for one season and then traded for fresh stock or sold to keep the blood-line strong.

Sometimes, mix-ups and mistakes occurred and sheep would be left behind on the mountain or rams escaped thus causing lambs to be dropped at the wrong time. It was only surprising that things didn't go wrong more often, considering the harsh climate and the rough terrain. The lamb that Benny was now holding was obviously one of these mistakes. It had been left till last for it was nearly fully grown but it had no ear markings and still supported a tail which was nearly as thick as its back leg. At first the men stood around scratching their heads trying to decide what to do with it. Now that the marking was finished, Rene had returned and was standing next to me. We listened to the discussion which was getting more intense and we tried to understand what was going on.

We were horrified when it became apparent that Benny was in favour of cutting off the fully grown tail while the rest of the men were against the idea. Benny was not one to back down after he had made up his mind, so, before anyone could stop him, he took a hasty swipe at the lamb's tail with his knife but struck the vertebrae. With the blood spurting out he tried again and then again before the tail finally lay on the ground, wriggling as if it had a life of its own. Blood continued to spray from the stump as Rene screamed and called Benny a bloody butcher before running into the house with tears streaming down her cheeks.

But I could not drag myself away and watched as Benny hesitated and then, changing position, he pulled back the sheep's head and cut its throat. With the jugular and the spinal chord cut, it died instantly. Leaving Emrys to carry on, Benny took the carcass into the farmhouse and laid it on the table in the back room. He sharpened his special knife and cut slits in the back legs of the dead sheep, near the shanks. He then inserted a tree, which looked like a big coat hanger, and suspended the carcass from a hook in the ceiling. I watched in awe as Benny removed the fleece with a few deft cuts of the knife, finishing with a few thumps of his fist and it came away cleanly in one piece. With a delicate cut, worthy of any surgeon, he slit open the belly without cutting the intestines. Then he inserted his hands into the cavity and removed all the guts in one attempt and let them fall into a bucket.

Seeing me standing there gaping, Benny sent me for some buckets of water with which he washed the carcass down. From around the intestines he removed the *cawl*, a thin fatty membrane, which resembled a fine lace apron. This he hung from the tree allowing it to drape over the exposed cavity of the sheep's rib cage. He then carefully gathered all the offal, including the lungs, or lights as they are known, and washed them clean of blood. These he put in the bucket for Mrs Ladd to put through her heavy old mincer. Benny said he would cut the carcass into joints after it had set overnight, and Mrs Ladd would make faggots or rissoles, by adding herbs to the mince and rolling them in the cawl. Everyone came in to admire Benny's butchering after finishing with the lambs. Even Emrys was impressed and said he was looking forward to Pen-rhiw's share, as all slaughtered meat was shared among the family. He couldn't help saying though that sheep were a lot easier to do than pigs, which was apparently Emrys's forte. We all enjoyed the rissoles though, even Rene.

The ewes with their marked lambs were left in a paddock near the house where they could be watched-over while they convalesced, and Rene and I were surprised at how little time it took for them to make a complete recovery. The weather was cool and dry which helped the healing process, unlike warm or wet weather which can be conducive to infection or blow fly strike.

Only a few days had passed before Mr Ladd told us that the sheep were ready to be returned to the mountain and would we like to accompany him, my job being to run ahead and open the gates.

It was a leisurely walk, Lil, ever alert, had nothing to do except follow in Mr Ladd's tracks as the sheep knew the way better than we did. It was the ewes that had the worrying time, however, trying to keep their lambs from straying as they ran and jumped and continually chased each other, showing no ill-effects of their recent ordeal. If by chance the mother and lamb were briefly united, the opportunity was taken for a quick refill, the lamb drawing on the teat and giving it a few head buts to speed up the supply. Then, re-energised, it would run and jump with the other lambs, leaving its mother looking rather bewildered.

Our pet lambs stayed together and I was pleased to see

them picking at the grass as they walked along, signifying a good chance of survival. I went to pat them but as I was not holding a milk bottle I was ignored. I couldn't blame them and as we watched the last sheep through the last gate onto the rugged mountain-side, I prayed that if there was such a thing as reincarnation I would not be sent back to earth as a Welsh lamb and especially not a male one.

The walk home was downhill with the turf soft and springy underfoot. We were surrounded by hills and on the high ground the white dots denoted sheep, and on the low land farm houses nestled in the patchwork fields where sleepy cattle lay. At this point, the valley gave the illusion that it could be jumped across but it was, in fact over two miles wide at the top. I could not help comparing our present surroundings with the concrete jungle we had been used to walking through on cement footpaths.

We could see Caersalem, our little chapel, and we stood in silence for a while undisturbed by any sound made by man. It was Mr Ladd who echoed our thoughts as he wondered how it was possible for the world to be at war when we were surrounded by so much peace and beauty.

All deep in their own thoughts, we strolled at a leisurely pace downhill toward what was our home and even Lil was happy to tag along, ignoring the scurrying rabbits for once. We had been following a dividing stone wall at the base of which a small stream flowed. The sound of trickling water attracted our attention so we paused to drink and splash ourselves with the cold water and, feeling refreshed, resumed our journey. Mr Ladd told us that the sheep would be brought down again before the end of summer, for shearing and dipping, and again we would be busy with the cropping and harvesting. He explained quietly how a good farmer looks after his animals and makes sure he puts away enough hay to feed them through the winter. He also said that he realised that some things seemed harsh to us, but, he patiently explained that if a sheep did not have its tail cut off, blowflies would lay their eggs in the stained wool in warm wet weather and then the maggots would eat the sheep alive. Also, if all the rams were allowed to breed, the flock would grow weaker and weaker and not be strong enough to survive the winter. It had been a long tiring day, but thankfully I noticed Rene had got over her previous hysterics.

When shearing could be put off no longer, the sheep were once again brought down from the mountain and held in a paddock next to the farmyard overnight. This allowed them to cool down before being shorn as it was easier to clip dry wool than wool wet with sweat. The next morning the sheep were herded into the farmyard where several men, including Emrys and Tom Selby, had come to help. Now the Welsh sheep has only a light coat of coarse wool as it is bred primarily for its fine meat, so it is not the hardest of sheep to shear. But the bending over and the use of hand shears still made it a back-breaking job. The dogs had the sheep pressed tightly in a temporary enclosure while the men stood around and finished their last smoke. Benny was putting the final touch to the edge of his blades and claiming his superiority as a shearer. An argument developed between Emrys and Benny which Mr Ladd tried to defuse to no avail. Bets were duly made as to who could shear the most sheep. Emrys was the shortest, so he had less distance to bend, also, his daily setting of one hundred rabbit traps had given him hands of steel. Emrys also had more experience as he had worked as a shearer at times to supplement his income. Benny though was younger and quick on his feet which would be an advantage when catching his sheep. He was also very determined and took any challenge most seriously. Emrys was a man of humour and unlike Benny was always quick to play a joke. Either way it was going to be a long day and the challenge would help remove some of the monotony.

Shearing at Dolrannog was carried out in the most basic manner, the shearers just grabbing a sheep from the pen and shearing it on the ground. Only the long wool was clipped from the sheep and allowed to fall on to the ground. The short wool under the belly and around the head and hocks was left on. When the shearing was finished the sheep was pushed through the gate into the adjoining field and another grabbed from the pen.

Rene was helping Mair pick up the long wool and stuffing it into sacks which I would jump on to press the wool down with my feet. When the sack was full to bursting, it was secured with clips and stored in the barn to await a buyer.

As the day progressed the men's backs began to ache and their hands became sore and they started to slow down. But not Benny, who was setting a cracking pace and keeping just ahead of Emrys, stopping only for lunch and tea breaks. During these breaks I noticed Emrys talking to the other men in a secretive manner, which resulted in them having silly grins on their faces. The men went back to work reluctantly at the end of the afternoon to finish the flock. But not Benny, who was keen to keep ahead of Emrys and seemed as fresh as when he started. Usually a tally was only kept for professional shearers who were paid so much per head, but because of their bet, a tally was kept on Benny and Emrys. They were still neck and neck when only the last three sheep remained and, as they both entered the pen taking a sheep each, the men all shouted that it was a draw. There was now only one sheep left and Tom Selby would claim this as he had almost finished the sheep he was shearing; the other shearers had inexplicably become very slow.

Suddenly, Tom Selby's shears flew out of his hand frightening his sheep which ran off with both Tom and his dog following. Emrys, who had not slowed down when a draw had been declared but in fact had speeded up, now surprised Benny by lifting his shorn sheep over the gate and grabbing the last sheep in the pen started shearing it. He then nonchalantly claimed victory by one sheep!

There were now no more sheep to shear and Benny looked non-plussed as he pushed his last sheep through the gate and watched Emrys shear the final one. The other men stood in a group smoking and talking and pretending to have no interest in the argument that had now developed between Benny and Emrys.

Looking over the gate at the shorn flock, Benny picked out a few sheep that had some tufts of wool left on them and accused Emrys of not shearing the sheep close enough. Emrys retaliated by calling Benny a butcher and of being responsible for all the cuts the sheep had endured during the day which now showed black after being painted with tar to prevent infection.

But, good humour prevailed and Benny produced the

stake, a packet of Woodbines, which he presented to Emrys. Emrys immediately opened the packet and passed them around with grand largesse urging the men to take several each and adding that opportunities to get a smoke out of Benny were rare indeed.

It had been a hot and tiring day but the sheep still had to be moved to the upper paddocks, where they would be held for a few days to allow any cuts to heal, then, after being dipped they would be returned to the mountain.

The cows had yet to be milked and the baby calves fed. It seemed that as the days grew longer, they also became more busy.

As spring turned to summer our first year at Dolrannog came to an end and we knew now, unlike twelve months ago, what to expect. Human nature allows bad times to be forgotten and good times to be remembered, but nothing could change the fact that we had seen our parents only once during that year. What little we knew about the war gave us no cause to be optimistic about returning home in the near future, indeed we had been told that Hitler had invaded Russia which did at least make the invasion of England less likely. We missed our home and our parents desperately, but we were developing a hardness like a scab on a sore. We had buried our feelings and could cope most of the time but underneath we were still hurting.

A few days later, after having been given time for their cuts to heal, the sheep were driven down to the valley for dipping. By law all sheep had to be dipped at least once a year to prevent a disease called sheep scab from infecting the flocks. It was extremely infectious and was spread by tiny mites. As usual, all who had time came with their dogs to lend a hand. Benny and Lil led the way along the narrow road at the bottom of the valley to where a barricade had been set up. Two flocks were ahead of us and soon there were other flocks behind as all the local farmers used the same dip on the same day. The reason for this was that the active ingredient in the yellow powder used in the dipping process was arsenic, so the local constable was on hand to make sure that none went astray and that the right amount was used. He then issued a signed certificate stating the number of sheep dipped by each farmer, for without this certificate sheep could not be moved or sold.

The truck collecting the milk churns had passed but now the road was completely blocked as the final flocks arrived. Anyone wishing to pass would have to make a detour of more than six miles, fortunately nobody did.

Each farmer's dog kept his flock separate, continually patrolling the gaps in between, tongue lolling, ears pricked, ever watchful and just daring any sheep to fall out of line.

The short waiting time gave the farmers an opportunity to compare flocks and stray sheep were returned to their rightful owners. There was much good natured banter among the men, however they were all very circumspect when discussing their dogs of whom they were most proud, a wrong word would start a fierce argument or worse.

Between the road and the stone wall that ran alongside it, a trough had been dug out and lined with small rocks and cemented. It was about fifteen paces long and deep enough to make a sheep swim though but too narrow to allow the sheep to turn around. At the near end, a stream was allowed to flow through the trough but this could be diverted around it by means of a temporary dam of a few small rocks. At the far end, the trough sloped up to a temporary pen where the sheep were held while they dried; the excess dip drained back into the trough.

Once the men got going the process was very quick. Sheep were kept pressed up against the barricade where a small gap between the fence and the post was the only way into the dip. Several men pushed, shoved or threw the sheep through the gap to land in the dip. Sometimes, though not often, the sheep would blindly follow each other and jump in of their own accord and then the man standing next to the dip would be hard pressed to make sure they were all completely dunked in the mixture, for which purpose he used a forked stick. The sheep would stumble up the slope snorting and shaking off the excess dip and as one pen emptied the other filled. The dripping sheep, who now had yellow coats, were released and the holding pen filled again. After each flock was dipped, the trough, if necessary, would be filled up and more yellow powder mixed and added, all under the watchful eye of Mr Plod.

It was a warm sunny day and the sheep suffered no ill effects apart from a few bruises and by the time we drove them back to the farm they were quite dry. We left the sheep in the yard while we all took refreshments in the house from where I was promptly ordered outside to wash my hands which somehow had managed to turn yellow.

Afterwards we helped draft the sheep, keeping back the fat lambs and some old wethers and ewes. These would be held and fattened for a few weeks in the fields before being sold; the rest of the flock were returned to the mountain.

I was glad we had pork in the *cawl* that night, I felt I had seen enough mutton for one day. Getting into bed, Rene held her nose saying I smelt like a newly-dipped sheep and I again wondered how my sister managed to stay so fresh and clean.

At breakfast, I listened as Rene asked Mr Ladd what had happened to the dip left in the trough and he explained how it was diluted by the water in the stream as it flowed into the river and out to sea. Still concerned, she asked if it could still kill the birds or fish and Mr Ladd assured her that it was too diluted to harm anything, but my thoughts centred on what Benny had complained about only a few days previously, and that was that salmon no longer swam up the river to spawn and even the trout were getting scarce.

Chapter 17

SUMMER

New England became an enigma for me, especially after I had questioned Mrs Ladd about it. She told us some tall tale about the wife having some terrible disease which caused her to swell up like an elephant and all the husband could do was sit and wait for her to burst. She warned us not to go near the place as the disease was contagious. We had never seen any sign of life there, never even any smoke rising from the single chimney. Yet the cottage did not look deserted and always appeared to be kept neat and tidy. One warm summer's day on our way home from school I made up my mind to look through the window of New England, as my curiosity overcame my trepidation. Rene became agitated and refused to wait for me, then suddenly she started screaming. I was surprised that she had become that upset and turned back towards her just in time to see a snake disappear into the hedgerow. It was a death adder and Rene was now completely hysterical as we had been told that they were extremely venomous and that a bite from one was fatal in a few moments. Rene had stepped on one as it lay sleeping in the sun looking like a dead stick. I was helpless. We were not near a stream and the only place

I could go was New England, but Rene wouldn't let me. She calmed down a little when we could find no sign of her having been bitten and after a while we were able to continue our journey. We stopped at the first stream to bathe her foot which still bore no sign of a bite. She was still shaking when we arrived at the farm. We told Mrs Ladd who said how lucky Rene was to still be alive, saying she thought the snake must have struck her shoe as adders were most aggressive. We kept a better lookout for them from then on with Rene becoming almost obsessed, but we never saw another snake.

It was the time of the year for the home-brew to be made. The big brass pan was emptied and cleaned; the same pan I was occasionally bathed in by the fire. It usually lived in the farmyard under the water spout for the animals to drink out of. It was placed on its triangular iron base and filled with fresh water from the well and a fire was lit under it. When it was boiling Mrs Ladd carefully measured the sugar she had been saving and stirred it in, followed by some hops and yeast. Twenty four hours later it was ready to be strained into the barrels. The first one, quite small, was put away for Christmas; the larger one would be drunk at the harvest in a few weeks' time as spring was now turning into summer.

The 21st of June, 1941 passed unnoticed by us. It was just another day, but in fact it marked the end of our first year in Wales and we were already aware that this was going to be a long war.

The second time round held no shocks or surprises; we had seen it all before, and the hardest thing we had to bear was our homesickness. We missed our parents desperately especially when it was bedtime and we would say our prayers and wonder when we would all be back together again. We had left home believing our absence was only for a short while, a matter of weeks but now we were thinking in years. We just had to live with our sadness.

Letter writing had become more difficult with all letters getting shorter and more sporadic. I found that the easiest way to fill up my obligatory one page was to draw a picture on half of it with any writing scrawled across the other half.

Although we had learned a few common phrases parrot fashion and could at times glean what subject or object was being discussed, there was no way we could participate in a Welsh conversation. This was most distressing on winter evenings when all were sitting around the fire. Welsh is a very difficult language to learn whether written or spoken and we made little effort to learn as we expected to be returning home almost on a daily basis to start with.

Then there was the isolated location and the long walks. With the approach of summer our resentment diminished. Our clothing became adequate as the days lengthened and became warm. Although still skinny we had grown tougher, and also wiser, the adage that familiarity breeds contempt certainly didn't apply to us on our walks up and down the mountain or any where else for that matter. We became weather-wise and though God tried to trick us at times, we were seldom caught in a squall or thunderstorm without cover. We learned to respect the mountain and its tantrums, especially in the winter. We still bore scars from chilblains but we could put up a good defence against acquiring any more.

During the last year we had become part of Dolrannog. The war had passed us by and living on a remote farm in Wales, surrounded by the most beautiful scenery, was a privilege indeed on a warm summer's day. Winter was another story.

We had come to terms with the animals and their idiosyncrasies. We could walk carefully past the gander without encroaching on his space and ignoring the hissing and flapping of wings. All dogs were respected and ignored, even though the neighbour's dogs still ran out and barked at us as we passed down the lane. All horses bit at one end and kicked at the other. Pigs had to be ringed and lambs docked. Rabbits had to be trapped or there would be no crops.

If the male calves were not sold off, the herd would become decimated, and if the cows were not regularly milked they would become dry and there would be no milk to sell. Mrs Ladd often told us that without the milk cheque there would be no Dolrannog and no food for us on the table, and I didn't like to be hungry.

The walk back to Dolrannog was a cross Rene and I had to bear but the strain was certainly eased with the arrival of summer. After a tiring day at school in winter we had to hurry home to beat the darkness of the short days, often running up the steep hill trying to keep ahead of an oncoming storm. So we appreciated the long summer days which allowed us to dawdle home, spending the time searching the hedgerows for berries or refreshing ourselves with cold water from a hidden mountain stream.

At the point where the farm land encroached on the mountain side, a stone wall extended a couple of hundred yards from the lane up to a ruined cottage. Not having had time or energy to explore before, on this day we followed a faint sheep trail around the biggest rocks and through the bracken alongside the wall. With its new cover of bright shiny bracken and the fresh yellow flowers of the prickly bush, the mountain had lost its forbidding appearance and we approached the ruins without any feeling of apprehension.

We were disappointed not to find anything at all as the ruins were very old and so, heeding my sister's warning of snakes I decided to look around for signs of other buildings. Then I saw the tree. It was not a large tree but it was loaded with the biggest black cherries I had ever seen. Calling to Rene, I hastily sampled some, after which I had to agree with her that they were not yet quite ripe, a fact confirmed by my stomach a few hours later. We decided to keep our find a secret and to wait for a couple of weeks before picking any more cherries, but on that day I couldn't contain myself and promised Mrs Ladd a big surprise when we arrived home from school.

We had scrounged enough paper bags for our purpose and by using our canvas lunch bag as well, we anticipated taking home a good haul. We ran most of the way to the cottage, quickly scrambling over the ruins to the tree. We could not believe our eyes but just stood looking at each other in amazement. Incredibly there was not one cherry left on the tree and it slowly dawned on us that somebody had beaten us to it!

I had to tell Mrs Ladd why she wasn't getting her surprise at which she seemed very relieved, telling us that the land with the tree on it belonged to the next farm down and undoubtedly they had picked the cherries to send to Cardigan Market. It had never occurred to us that anyone owned the land.

However, we were well aware of who owned the property with the plum trees, but I have to admit it didn't deter us from sharing some of them for a while. We preferred to be outside on summer evenings, the long twilight seemed to make the inside of the house more gloomy, so on this particular evening we followed the cows to their field after milking, having agreed to inspect the hedgerows to see how the hazelnuts were ripening. The field next to us belonged to the neighbouring farm and in the corner nearest the lane were two large plum trees, standing next to the ruins of a small cottage. We had already taken some to Mrs Ladd who told us never to go near the place again, although we all enjoyed the plums stewed with custard and cream.

As more plums ripened so the temptation to disobey Mrs Ladd's orders grew, until I could no longer just look at the plums. I had to have some, and Rene reluctantly followed me as I climbed over the gate and up a tree where we were out of sight. This had now become our evening ritual, I always climbed higher than Rene. We had carefully checked out the field. As a rule, we could only see a few heifers and calves grazing contentedly and ignoring us completely, but on this particular occasion the field was empty. As usual I was passing the ripest plums down to Rene who was sitting swinging her legs on a lower branch but we both froze as we heard the sound of a motor vehicle approaching and were shocked when a light truck stopped at the gate. One of our neighbours got out of the truck, opened the gate and the truck backed up to it. The two men then lowered the back of the truck to form a ramp down which a very angry bull charged.

The men watched the bull as he tried to jump the fence to get amongst our cows, then satisfied that he was well secured in the field after checking the gate and closing the back of the truck, they drove off. Frustrated at being closed in, the bull came charging up the fence line and gave the gate a few good head butts which sent Rene up the tree as high as me. Her movement had caused the bull to see us and he gave our tree the same treatment as the gate sending plums falling like a shower of rain. After having expended his energy the bull then stood at the gate and kept his beady eyes on us.

In spite of my bombarding him with the greenest and hardest plums, the bull wouldn't move and there was no way we were going to climb down and face him. It was not at all comfortable sitting in the tree and as it started to get dark Rene began to get upset. We were both very glad to hear Benny coming down the lane and calling out to us.

After ascertaining that we were unharmed and then realising our predicament, all Benny could do was laugh. He thought it very funny and kept asking if we thought we were monkeys. He was laughing so much that he had to keep wiping the tears from his eyes.

By this time Ferdinand, the bull, had settled down and was more interested in some lush grass growing around him. Benny casually climbed the gate and gave the bull a couple of slaps on the rump and it just strolled away. Even so, it took very little time for Rene and I to get down from the tree and run to the gate. To give Benny his dues though, it was he who told Mrs Ladd that Rene and I had just taken longer than we thought to return home after our walk. That was the end of our plums; we decided we had had enough.

Our second summer on Dolrannog was rather boring for me. We missed Megan and Rene and Mona became even closer friends, leaving me the odd one out. During the school holidays I would join them and walk to the shop at Ty'n Rhos or the little Post Office but I was clearly a nuisance to them and my presence would cause them to talk to each other in whispers invariably followed by giggles. If I did join them in a game I was disadvantaged by two votes to one, as, when playing hospitals one would be the doctor, the other the nurse and I was always the patient. I soon learned to leave them to themselves and I would tag along with Benny or Mr Ladd where possible, otherwise I retreated to my world of make believe where I was free to do as I pleased.

We all worked together in the fields at harvest time and I, of course, now considered myself quite competent to do any of the jobs. I was quite adept at harnessing the horses to the various machines or carts, but was strictly forbidden to sit on the mower or hay rake. Mrs Ladd constantly reminded me of some boy who had fallen into the blade of a mower to be instantly converted into minced meat and eaten by the dogs. When I asked which farm it had happened on she was unable to remember and when I asked Benny, he didn't know either. I did keep off the machines but felt quite proud standing in the empty cart, reins in hand, guiding Prince back to the paddock for another load of hay or sheaves of corn, even though Mr Ladd was holding on to the bridle!

All too quickly the summer holidays came to an end and it was time to resume our daily walk to school. As if Huey had been waiting for us, during the very first week it poured. He turned the tap on and it rained for three days.

On the first morning we were lucky, as the cows had been held back in the cowshed after milking for the vet to give them one of their regular tests for T.B. This was an anxious time for all the farmers because if the tests proved positive they were unable to sell that milk or stock, and in a severe outbreak they could even be forced to destroy all their stock.

The vet's car was standing in the rain getting its usual washing by the hand of God and we were standing in the porch as the vet sloshed his way under his brolly from the cowshed to his car.

Mrs Ladd came out of the house and called the vet to come in for a cup of tea as was customary, but he declined saying he was very busy and running late but on seeing Rene and me ready for school, he indicated for us to get into his car. I didn't listen to what Mrs Ladd was saying about speed and whisky but dashed across the farmyard and climbed in through the back door of the car, which the vet had opened from the inside. I was finding room on the back seat rather scarce and I was about to ask if I could sit in the front when I quickly realised there was even less room there.

Inside, the car was full of papers, boxes, syringes, ointments, and bottles of peculiar looking liquids, all scattered over the seats and floor. Calling to my sister to hurry as she was still standing hesitantly next to Mrs Ladd on the porch, the vet instructed me to make more room on the back seat by putting more things on the floor. I knew the car was a Rover and it was not that old. The interior still had a nice leathery smell mixed with the smell of carbolic, tobacco smoke from the vet's pipe and whisky. The walnut trim was still shiny and the array of dials on the dashboard was impressive. The exterior paintwork was showing British racing green as the rain washed the mud away. The vet's hands were nervously tapping on the wheel as if he was waiting for a race to start rather than giving a couple of kids a lift to school. He rectified this by taking a flask out of his inside pocket and giving himself a good slug as Rene climbed in next to me looking a little apprehensive as she saw him replacing his flask.

We knew little about Mr Howells, the vet, other than that he lived in one of the houses we passed on our way to school. What had attracted my initial attention was the Rover which was usually parked at the side of the house and being one of the very few cars around. The house was a little larger than most but typical of the area with slate roof and built from the local grey stone. An overgrown garden was enclosed by a dry stone wall.

The vet lived alone in this two storeyed house, his lovely wife having died in tragic circumstances. They were very much in love and her death had devastated him. They had only one child, a daughter, as beautiful as her mother. She was away at college and only came home for holidays. In her absence, he found solace in a bottle of scotch which was his constant companion. His only other pleasure was derived from driving his car at high speed, much to the consternation of the locals and the police. By the same token every farmer in the district would swear he was the best vet ever known and had never failed to attend any call, day or night, regardless of the weather. His thin face was reflected in the driving mirror, an unhealthy grey, prematurely lined, with his smelly pipe jutting out between his thin lips, and topped by a greasy deerstalker hat. His thin body was too small inside his clothes.

Leaning forward, he turned the key and the engine sprung into life. It was as if he had also sprung into life with the car as we quickly and smoothly accelerated down the lane spraying mud from the rear wheels and causing the geese and ducks to scatter in alarm. Too late to wave goodbye to Mrs Ladd who was hiding behind her pinny in alarm on the porch.

We had passed the neighbouring farm before the dogs heard us coming. Without reducing speed we joined the road, down a couple of gears and we were past the ruined castle and the church, a couple of blasts on the horn miraculously cleared the narrow street through the village as we sped past the police station and making a U turn, we were deposited right outside the front of the hall. Without giving us time to say thank you he was off again just as the flying squad appeared in the doorway of the police station, buttoning up his jacket before mounting his push-bike. The rain had stopped; we had been less than five minutes in the car and now, as we walked to meet Miss Foy, we could see her surprise. Rene and I were not only the first to school but we were also still dry; an achievement never to be repeated.

Of all the hundreds of times we made that journey there was only one other time that we had a lift, but that was later when the brothers on the neighbouring farm acquired a car or should I say a wreck. It was a small two door sportscar that had seen better days. Although originally built low to the ground it was now even lower as the springs were flat. We had just passed their gate to the usual snarling from their dogs when this battered looking car pulled up and offered us a lift. At first Rene declined but I climbed in so she had to follow. Conversation was impossible over the noise and vibration of the engine. Every bump we went over caused the car to bottom with a bone crunching thump. Fumes came into the car as the exhaust pipe had long since become dislodged. As we approached the steepest descent it became obvious that we had no brakes as the driver's right foot went flat to the floor on the brake pedal, the hand brake pulled hard in his left hand and although the car was in gear with the ignition off, we were still gaining speed. Trying to steer around the bend with one hand almost ended in disaster. We were shaking when we got out and politely thanked the driver. The car didn't go for long, and was left standing in their yard, visible through the gate where we saw it every time we walked by. We needed no reminding of that trip though!

Chapter 18

AUTUMN

Summer turned to autumn and we checked all our favourite spots to see if the nuts had ripened and ate the last of the blackberries and the wild strawberries. The days grew shorter and the weather changed to warn us of worse things to come. This was a depressing time for us. The war news was not good, Hitler was sweeping across Russia after occupying most of Europe. There was no mention of another visit from our parents and Christmas was not far off.

At the hall Miss Foy tried to lift our spirits but her production of the 'Pirates of Penzance' suffered a severe set-back when the twin brother and sister who were playing the leading roles returned to London. By this time we were all sick of the songs, having heard them a hundred times. These were then replaced by Christmas carols which were sung without much enthusiasm as nothing could make the dim smelly hall look or feel much like Christmas. Nor, in all honesty, could our singing compare with any of the local school or chapel choirs which could be heard throughout the village.

Once again we resumed our never ending battle of

drying wet clothing with our raincoats capable of protecting us only from the lightest showers. We walked bare-headed and bare-legged, putting on an extra jumper only in the coldest weather along with woollen scarves and gloves. This was sufficient if it was dry, but wet wool does not keep out chilling winds. Our socks would soak up the water so our shoes would always be damp, no matter how thick we applied the Dubbin on the outside, and this caused them to come apart. Our woollen clothing would still be damp the next morning and be most uncomfortable to put on. No wonder we looked forward to the weekends, even though there was little to do inside as the farmhouse was always dim, especially in the winter months.

Relief was at hand when one Friday, after a trip to the village, Mr Ladd returned and placed a cardboard box on the table. Everyone gathered around in excitement as he carefully unpacked the box to reveal a shiny Tilly lamp. It looked like any other hurricane lamp except that it was chromed. Everyone stood admiring it as Benny read out the instructions which were in English. The difference between this lamp and an ordinary paraffin lamp was that the new one was pressurised by means of a pump fitted in the base, like a Primus stove and it had a mantle instead of a wick. It also needed preheating with methylated spirits which had to be poured into a cup under the mantle. The lamp came with a small packet of spare mantles. Sliding the glass up, Benny took a mantle from its packet and with thick fumbling fingers finally attached it by its silken thread. A mantle is made of fine silk mesh in the shape of a tiny purse and is attached to the end of the pressure pipe by a strand of silk threaded around the opening, pulled tight and then tied. The base was filled with paraffin and the cap under the mantle filled with methylated spirits. As per instructions, the base was pressurised by means of some vigorous action on the pump before lighting the meths. This caused the silken mantle to flare and shrink into a white calcified mesh. The meths burned away in a few minutes preheating the pipe and mantle. Benny quickly turned on the valve which allowed paraffin vapour to exude into the mantle which immediately gave off a dazzling white light. With 'Ohs' and 'Ahs' everyone looked around in wonder; never had the kitchen seen such light. Everything stood out so clearly and even the cobwebs in the corners became visible. As a performer responds to applause so Benny couldn't resist an encore, and pumped even harder, causing the lamp to make an even louder hissing noise. Mrs Ladd now cried out in alarm for him to stop but, alas, on his last heavy push down on the pump his hand slipped causing the lamp to jerk and the delicate mantle to shatter. This caused the glass to smoke up as the vapour now burned without a mantle and the lamp was getting very hot. Benny was just able to turn off the valve, burning his fingers in the process, before carrying the thing, which was treated as a time bomb, outside. The oil cloth on the table was marked by black rings and smoking but Mrs Ladd dealt with that problem simply by pouring the milk from a nearby jug over it. The room was even darker now and filled with smoke and the smell of paraffin oil.

Benny then came back inside looking as if he had just auditioned for the minstrel show and everyone started shouting at once. It was more than half an hour before the lamp was cool enough to bring inside again. It had to be dismantled and washed to get rid of the black carbon on the glass and chrome, and Rene was given the job of tying another silk mantle in place. Mrs Ladd would not allow Benny to light the lamp inside again, so he did it in the porch, this time with less pressure and not too much trouble.

Until the novelty wore off Benny became more attached to his lamp than Florence Nightingale had been to hers. The final straw, however, came when he took it to the cowshed where the cows were waiting to be milked. As he walked with it across the yard, Mrs Ladd yelled at him to put it out as he was attracting all the German bombers, but to no avail. As he entered the cowshed with the bright hissing light, all the cows with one accord tried to pull free from their bales, rolling their eyes and flattening their ears in terror. Unable to escape, they then lifted their tails and in unison evacuated everything they could. Mr Ladd, who had already started milking one cow, had his back to the far wall and had no way of escape. He didn't exactly come out smelling of roses. It took an hour and an extra ration of cattle cake before the cows settled down and gave milk, during which time the cowshed also had to be hosed out. During this debacle the lamp had received another knock which created the need for yet another new mantle.

Eventually the experiment with modern lighting was deemed a failure. The menthylated spirits would run out or the mantles would be hard to come by because of the wartime shortages. The lamp was kept on show though, having pride of place just inside the kitchen door and hanging from the ceiling at just the right height to hit anyone who didn't notice it on the head.

A compromise was reached when the parlour lamp was exchanged with the kitchen lamp. The only difference being that the parlour lamp had two wicks instead of one. This certainly did not equate with it providing twice the light and indeed the difference was only marginal. It also required twice the wick trimming otherwise it would produce twice the smoke and give out an even poorer light.

As soon as I opened my eyes that morning I knew there was snow; I had seen the same light before. The light coming through the little window was white, whiter than the light from the Tilly lamp. I jumped over my sister, waking her of course, and surveyed the scene through the little window. We had had a heavy fall; everything was covered by a thick white blanket and all was silent. There was no lane and no hedgerows; all were buried under the snow. My first thoughts were no more school and we would not be taking part in the carol concert since we were due to start our Christmas holidays in a few days time. I also realised we would be having a white Christmas unless the snow melted quickly.

After hastily dressing, I ran down the stairs, stood in the porch and made my first snowball, but there was nothing moving to throw it at so I went inside to warm my hands at the fire. Mrs Ladd was sitting there holding a cup of tea and wearing a worried look on her face. She told me that there was plenty of time for milking now as there was no way the milk truck could get through and that the road along the bottom of the valley might not be passable for days. This was a serious setback as Dolrannog's main income was the milk cheque and no milk meant no milk cheque.

Rene appeared looking fresh and bright as always and asked Mrs Ladd if the postman would be able to get through, for we had not heard from our parents for some time and we were expecting to hear from them in time for Christmas. We had posted them our hand-made Christmas cards weeks ago. Mrs Ladd looked doubtful but not wishing to disappoint us said the snow sometimes melted quickly but she certainly gave us no cause for optimism.

Having experienced the whole gamut of the weather over many years of farming high upon the mountainside, Dolrannog was not caught unprepared for a heavy fall of snow. Routine preparations for the winter were carried out year after year.

The hardy Welsh mountain sheep were bred to survive in harsh conditions and most of the losses occurred because of hungry foxes and other animals and birds of prey. These were acknowledged as a fact of life and kept under control by regular shoots on the mountain which were carried out by the neighbouring farmers in the spring and summer. Usually, the sheep would find shelter on the lee side of a rock or promontory and find something to eat on the exposed slopes where the wind kept the land almost free of snow. If, by chance sheep were buried in a snow drift it was not uncommon for them to survive in their little snow cave for up to three weeks.

Apart from a lack of exercise, the horses and cows lived in comfort. The horses remained in the stable, which was cleaned twice a day and fresh straw put down for their bed. They were given water and hay and a few oats, and it was always warm inside the stable.

The cowshed and barn both being under one roof were separated by a low internal wall. This made it easy to pass the hay and cattle cake to each cow. As the cows stayed in overnight during winter anyway, they felt quite content to be inside through the days as well. After it had been hosed down the cowshed smelt sweet with fresh hay and clean straw.

As the sweepings from the cowshed were shovelled onto the manure heap the chickens would squabble and scratch over the pickings and the snow around would soon become stained.

The geese and ducks took shelter in the derelict building and were given some warm mash at night; the flock having been culled to just breeding stock. There were no calves to feed, just heifers who were fed outside the cowshed and there were only the three pigs kept for breeding in their sties. Snow was shovelled to make tracks from the house to the various buildings and the wood pile, which had been chopped and stacked in readiness against the farm house wall and would last longer than the snow.

Our world had shrunk to being within the perimeter of the farmyard.

Life became tedious. Highjacking Benny and bombarding him with snowballs soon lost its appeal after being met with quick and forceful retaliation. We would help with the morning and evening chores but it became hard to occupy ourselves during the day, so it was a pleasant surprise when Emrys appeared carrying a shovel and followed by the rest of his family. Mona and Rene paired off into a corner to chat away and I soon got fed up of listening to the others talking about the snow in Welsh and went outside.

It was cold and lightly snowing so I thought I would go to the loft in the barn which was warm, being over the cowshed. I made my way to the barn door where I was confronted with the gander who had brought his gaggle of geese out for a peck around the manure heap. We eyed each other off. I had the choice of going back or pushing past the gander who was now preparing for battle, neck extended close to the ground, hissing, and beating his wings. I had been intimidated by this monster for eighteen months so giving vent to all my fears, frustrations and disappointments with a mighty yell, I charged and tried to land a good kick. I don't know who was most surprised when he flew straight up in the air and over my head! I didn't wait around but dived at the barn door and fumbled to find the wooden wedge which acted as the lock. Then, I saw, to my horror, that the monster had landed and was again charging at me. I turned and ran to the open door of the cowshed which, fortunately, was only a few paces away, slamming the door behind me and waking all the cows in fright. I was shaking and the geese were making a terrible noise as I entered the barn and climbed up the ladder to the loft. There was a small window at floor level overlooking the yard towards the house and directly over the cowshed door. I lay down and looked out; nobody had come to investigate the noise and after a while I got up and in the dim light started to inspect my surroundings. This was one of my favourite hiding places and I had looked around it many times before and there was nothing I had missed; it was really quite uninteresting unless you had a good imagination. There were the usual bags and boxes, pieces of harness and all the bits and pieces that were never thrown away incase they might be useful. But on this day my eyes nearly popped, for on the floor, in full view, was a gun! I was quite sure it hadn't been there on any of my previous visits. I knew I should go away and just leave it alone but could not resist picking it up, albeit very gingerly, and not touching the trigger. I knew very little about guns but could see this was not a shotgun. I then noticed a tobacco tin on the floor which contained lead pellets. I knew then I had an air gun in my hands and with more confidence I opened it and looked through the barrel in the dim light. The gun was obviously old but the barrel was not rusty so I loaded the gun with just air and pulled the trigger. It seemed to work all right so I inserted a slug and loaded it again. Lying down and pointing the gun out of the window, I looked for a target and there was the gander smack in the centre of my sights. I hesitated, wondering how powerful the gun was. I didn't want to kill it. I also wondered how accurate the sights were. I didn't want to hit him in the eye. But the temptation was too strong and trying to still my shaking hands, I carefully aimed at the middle of the gander's body where the strongest wing feathers were, and pulled the trigger. I had the intense satisfaction of seeing the bird jump two feet in the air emitting a squawk of surprise, then on landing chafing his wing feathers with his beak. Ten seconds later I couldn't control my laughter as he performed an encore at my command. After several more repeats, the other geese stood around the gander with quizzical looks in their eyes before ignoring him and making their way back to the building. As he turned to follow I gave him the last two slugs in his tail feathers. On looking at the empty tin, I realised that the gander must be carrying over a dozen slugs in his anatomy. I just hoped he wouldn't die of lead poisoning.

Now wishing that I hadn't used all the pellets, I placed the empty tin and the gun back where I had found them and returned to the house. I never mentioned the gun to anyone, not even Rene, and when I next entered the loft it was nowhere to be seen. I came to the conclusion that Benny used it for shooting rats. The gander appeared not to have suffered any ill effects and I began to wonder if I had dreamed it all.

Chapter 19

ANOTHER CHRISTMAS IN WALES

Over the next few days more snowfalls kept Dolrannog in isolation and soon all the milk churns were full to overflowing. Mona came over to help Mrs Ladd churn out butter and make cheese. Rennet was added to the milk that was left to settle in a large wooden tub and the curds and whey were separated.

There was not a lot wasted, but even I knew there was a limit as to how much custard and cream I could devour and eventually the pigs reaped the benefit, and put on weight.

Rene and I had missed the last few days of school, so we had also missed the carol singing and the end of term Christmas party, which worried us not at all. But we did become anxious about our mail from home. We had not received anything for quite a while and we were expecting some contact for Christmas and my birthday on Christmas Eve, which was now only one day away. When we asked Mrs Ladd if she thought Mr Davies would be able to get through on his bike she was unable to give us much hope and, as if to confirm her opinion, it started to snow again.

We knelt on the old couch watching the snow falling

through the little window, feeling rather sorry for ourselves. There was nothing in the kitchen to remind us of Christmas, no Christmas cards on the dresser shelves, and no decorations. It was too late now to hear from home. Then Lil started barking. At first we could see nothing, and then something was moving in the lane and as it passed through the gate we saw it was Mr Davies, the Post, and his wonderful bike, which he was steadfastly pushing through the snow. Not bothering with coats, we rushed out to greet him in great excitement. He was rather out of breath and was emitting little puffs of steam like a steam engine. Catching his breath, he delved into his post bag and produced our letters and parcels which he handed to us wishing us a happy Christmas with a big smile. We couldn't thank him enough and felt guilty that it was only on our account that he had had to make such a difficult trip. Refusing Mrs Ladd's offer of refreshment, he turned his heavy bike around and disappeared in the snow.

We didn't see Mr Davies very often and never on school days, but he was out and about in all weather and never missed a delivery. He was our only link with our parents and he became a real friend. On the days he had mail for the Ladds but none for us he always had a warm smile and words of encouragement; it was as if he too not only shared our times of happiness but also our disappointments.

He was a small bird like man, always neatly dressed in his dark blue uniform with collar and tie and his cap set squarely on his head. His trousers were neatly held by bicycle clips just above his leather boots which somehow always remained shiny. The old-fashioned red Post Office bike looked far too big and heavy for him, especially when loaded with mail. This he kept in a large leather satchel in front of the handlebars and on rainy days he would envelop himself and the mail bag in a tent-like yellow oilskin. In windy weather this would make it even more difficult to control the bike as the oilskin acted like a sail. Perhaps that is why Mr Davies, the Post, as he was known, pushed the bike more than rode it. Also, he must have had one of the most tortuous mail routes in the UK, being mostly on unmade roads that twisted and turned uphill and down dale with very few flat spots in-between. He may have been rewarded by the fact that he also had one of the most scenic routes and that his job allowed him time to appreciate the beautiful countryside in its ever changing seasons, though I must admit to wondering why he didn't ride a horse. Perhaps it would have been too hard on the horse.

We went inside and opened our mail. We had the usual Christmas cards to share around and small articles of clothing which were our presents. I also received a card for my birthday. Rene and I were relieved to know that our parents were still safe, but looking around the kitchen it didn't seem much like Christmas. The Ladds, however, were overjoyed and to them Mr Davies was Santa Claus as he had been able to inform them that the milk truck would be through later. Although it was unable to follow its normal route along the bottom of the valley it could get through by taking the road along the top.

So Prince was harnessed up to the heavy cart since the load was too much for Turpin and the float, and everyone lined up to wave Benny goodbye. Scott did not have a better send off when he left for the South Pole, but I'm glad to say Benny's journey ended more successfully.

The next day being Christmas Eve and my birthday, the family gathered together and Mr Ladd made a fine speech about the war causing people to change their homes and lives and hoping for peace to come soon so families could be reunited and spend their Christmases together again. He then presented me with a beautiful bone-handled pocket knife, a present from all the family. I was surprised when he asked me for a penny saying it was an old Welsh custom and meant that the knife was a gift of friendship and not a threat. To me a penny seemed rather a large amount to give away and since I only had a halfpenny that was accepted.

I was duly warned that the knife was very sharp and it was also very stiff making it hard to open the blade. In the end Benny had to open it for me. The family eagerly watched my reaction, hoping that I appreciated such a fine knife and although I was a little overawed by being the centre of so much attention I managed my thank you's in the proper manner. I finished my performance by demonstrating my ability to close the knife and simultaneously take a slice off my little finger. The resulting flow of blood brought about some quick action and later everyone marvelled at how much blood had escaped through such a small cut. While my finger was still sore and bandaged Benny offered to look after the knife for me. With use, he said, the spring would become weaker making it easier for me to use later. This I happily agreed to but Benny must have had a lot of trouble weakening the spring and I never did get the knife back from him. Secretly I was very relieved by this arrangement!

I had just had my finger bandaged when Mona arrived.

Rene and I were glad of the diversion as we were wondering what to do with ourselves. Because the house was not looking at all like Christmas we were not at all filled with the Christmas spirit and in fact were rather down in the dumps but Mona soon changed that. She was well wrapped up with a long scarf around her neck and, telling us to dress likewise, she told us we were going carol singing. It was a cold crisp day and although it had stopped snowing there were still deep drifts along the hedgerows. Benny had left earlier on his bike using it more like a snow plough than riding it. Mrs Ladd had tried to stop him saying he would surely have an accident on the way but had now resigned herself to dozing next to the fire where Mr Ladd was already snoring on the settle opposite. So Rene and I were glad to follow Mona out of the house. We walked to Pen-rhiw where we held a rehearsal under Mona's instructions. I was not very keen on the idea of tramping through the snow singing carols outside farmhouse doors until I heard money being mentioned and food and drinks. So with my interest now fully aroused, I sang with such enthusiasm that even Mona told me to pipe down and she could out-sing anyone. Mona told us to sing what words we knew in Welsh and hum the rest of the lines, but it didn't take long for us to learn as we only sang three carols, starting with 'Good King Wenceslas' followed by 'Silent Night'. If we were acknowledged and given money and/or sustenance we would finish up with 'While Shepherds Watched'.

After some adjustments outside Pen-rhiw, Mona was reasonably happy with our performance. Rene's voice could now be heard as she had gained confidence with me being quietened down a little. It was not difficult to follow Mona's lead as we kept time by stamping our feet and clapping our hands which also helped us to keep warm. The effect of this was to make even 'Silent Night' sound like one of Bodicea's battle hymns. Thank goodness the farmhouses had heavy doors and thick walls. Mair and Emrys came out and pronounced our little choir fit to go on the road and Emrys insisted on giving us a penny each and Mair presented us with a hot Welsh cake. We set off scrambling down a narrow path to the bottom of the valley to our first objective, a farm called Llannerch, where we were received most unkindly by several large vicious dogs. I was alarmed, to say the least, when one grabbed the heel of my shoe and I was more than ready to return home when Mona came to the rescue. She shouted at the dogs in Welsh and they simply dropped their tails and ran away leaving us alone to sing our carols. My voice was now contributing a distinct tremolo effect to the sound of the choir.

After our second carol the door was opened and we went inside. We were plied with food and drinks and also the inevitable questions but we now had another problem which was how to get away from our generous hosts. An hour later we sang our farewell carol with our hearts filled with gratitude towards our kind friends and our stomachs overfilled with their generosity. As we struggled through the snow to our next farm we made a resolution not to accept any more invitations into the houses.

And so the day passed. Only one farm ignored us but we were not upset as Mona laughingly suggested that they may have been having an afternoon sleep. We arrived back at

Dolrannog just before dark with our feet frozen and as the circulation returned to our fingers and toes the pain from our chilblains nearly sent us mad. We had walked almost ten miles so Mona told everyone and had lost count of how many farms we had sung at.

However, all our aches and pains were forgotten as we emptied our money on to the table. We had made our fortunes! Mona insisted we each had an equal share even though it had been her idea and Rene and I just followed along. Everyone gathered around as we counted out the coins into three separate piles and, after counting out my share six times to be sure I found I had the grand sum of three shillings and three pence halfpenny. I was rich! This was the most money by far that I had ever possessed in my life. Then, I realised there was precious little for me to spend my new found wealth on, apart from a few peppermints or bullseyes. When Rene and I next visited Ty'n Rhos we bought tobacco for Mr Ladd and a packet of Woodbines for Benny. We found some beeswax for Mrs Ladd and put it in her sewing basket.

Rene and I woke up late on Christmas morning and since there was no sound in the house the milking was taking place as usual. Our legs ached and our chilblains itched and our thoughts were about Christmases in happier times. The house looked even more gloomy as we went downstairs, our Christmas cards on the dresser being the only decorations. We wondered where our parents were on this Christmas day and couldn't believe that a year had passed since we had last seen them in this very room. I looked at my sister and saw tears in her eyes and knew she was feeling as miserable as I was but I couldn't think of anything to say to cheer her up. I felt cold and moved closer to the fire as Mrs Ladd came into the house through the back door carrying the yellow enamel jug filled with fresh milk.

The men followed behind her and we all wished each other a Merry Christmas, then, with the broom handle, Mrs Ladd unhooked a leg of ham from the ceiling saying we would have a Christmas treat. Rene and I watched as Mrs Ladd started cutting generous slices. The dark outside skin was removed first to reveal bright pink meat covered in a layer of snow white fat. The big black frying pan was spitting on the stove in readiness and I could feel my mouth watering in anticipation but I saw that Rene had a look of horror on her face. I followed her gaze and could hardly believe my eyes, the beautiful ham was now discharging a steady stream of maggots in a flow of putrid green liquid.

Mrs Ladd cried out in alarm and everyone stood around giving advice and making comments. Benny took the ham and knife from his mother and proceeded to chop away the infested parts which were thrown out through the door for Lil who immediately showed her surprise and gratitude at sharing our Christmas breakfast by gulping it down and wagging her tail for more.

It had been a larger ham than usual, and apparently, although it had been buried in salt and rubbed every day for weeks before being smoked in the chimney, a blow fly had struck during the summer. There was nothing amiss with the taste or texture of the slices of ham that Mrs Ladd finally cooked for breakfast. Mr Ladd and Benny certainly enjoyed their servings but, somehow, Rene and I had lost out appetite and once again I was able to sneak our share to Lil who was delighted to receive a second helping. The much reduced ham was put back into a bed of salt in the dairy and later hung to be smoked again in the chimney from where, no doubt, it was made into *cawl*.

After breakfast I helped Benny clean out the stable and cowshed and feed all the animals and after the firewood had been carried inside Benny said he was going up the mountain to check on the sheep. Rene was writing letters so I was glad of the excuse of helping Benny to get out of the house.

The snow was not so deep now but there were still drifts against the walls and outcrops. It was under these drifts that sheep could be buried and it was our job to find them. For this purpose Benny was carrying a light shovel and had equipped each of us with a long thin stick to be used for probing the deeper drifts to feel if there were any sheep buried. We would also look for air holes in the snow and Lil would tell us if there were any sheep buried by digging with her front paws. At first she had been reluctant to accompany us but now followed closely behind Benny, walking in his footsteps.

We reached the top fence-line which was hardly distinguishable as the snow had drifted over it; this was our main target area. With difficulty I climbed over and disappeared into the drift. I was wet and cold by the time I extracted myself but this was of no concern to Benny who couldn't stop laughing. Fortunately the day was not too cold, the sun shone weakly and there was no chill wind. We prodded, looked and listened as we followed the fence line for a couple of miles without finding any distressed sheep.

Benny pointed up the mountain to a large flock of sheep in the distance, and a look of relief came over his face as he said that, without a doubt, they belonged to Dolrannog and apparently had not strayed but stayed together and obviously not suffering any great loss. How he could surmise all this at such a long distance I couldn't understand but we were both happy to retrace our steps back home. On Christmas day, our lunch was the usual bread and a bowl of *cawl*, but after the long cold walk it seemed to taste extra good.

Rene and I were set for a boring afternoon but things brightened up with the arrival of Emrys and his family and also Tom Selby with his. There was much talking which as usual we were not part of, but we did join in with the singing of the Christmas carols and the traditional Welsh songs.

We also joined in the early tea with copious quantities of hot Welsh cakes and pancakes straight from the griddle plate over the fire. I also enjoyed the cold fruit pies and custard. They all left early for milking and to put the little people to bed, leaving us with our own thoughts about Christmas. I was thinking about last Christmas when our parents visited and we had spent the day in front of the fire in the parlour when I remembered my train set and felt the urge to look at it again. I climbed the stairs and pulled the box out from under the bed. It was covered in dust as I hadn't touched it in months. I quickly formed the track into its small circle on the table on which I placed the two carriages. I then wound up the clockwork engine and watched the train go round and round. Everyone watched briefly but quickly became bored. It wasn't long before I too became bored with it and was about to pack it up when Benny had one of his brilliant ideas and suggested we turned the track into an obstacle course and make the train go up and downhill like a scenic railway in a fair ground.

This we did by placing various objects under the lines to make the track uneven, then I wound the engine up tightly for optimum power and placed it on the track. The train jumped the rails before it had ever travelled half of the circuit, spilling its metal innards all over the flagstone floor. As I bent down to pick up the pieces I felt tears come to my eyes. Not tears of disappointment over the loss of my train set, which I didn't much enjoy anyway, but tears of self pity and, looking at my sister I could see she was equally upset too.

Lying next to each other in bed on that Christmas night we both wondered what next Christmas would bring and where we would be. Waiting for sleep to arrive and bring me dreams of home, I lay remembering all the other Christmases which I had spent so happily with my family in Battle. So far away, so long ago.

Chapter 20

WINTER IN WALES
1942

The new year was welcomed with a family gathering and it was good to see Wynfred and Megan again. The last of the home brew was drunk and along with harvesting, was the only time alcohol was brought into the house. Rene and I joined in the singing and discovered we had quite a repertoire of hymns and traditional Welsh songs, although we were not familiar with all the words. As usual Benny's rendition of 'Danny Boy' stole the limelight.

The snow eventually disappeared only to be replaced with rain and cold winds. This kept us indoors most of the time which became rather boring, so it was with mixed feelings that we fronted up for our walk to school on the first day of the new term.

Our meagre wardrobe had been supplemented with parcels from home, but we still lacked raincoats that were really waterproof and no matter how thickly we coated our shoes with Dubbin they never kept our feet dry, and we were always banging Blackies into the soles of our shoes trying to keep them together.

The hedgerows were wet and bare and it was a wet

uncomfortable journey we made on most days. On the uphill climb home, with heads down, we would walk and run as quickly as possible, having to stop occasionally to catch our breath.

Stopping at the big rocks where I had waited for the steam engine, I showed Rene the arrow that was carved on one and we found another carved on a large rock by the gate just near the farmhouse. As we stood by the fire changing our clothes, Rene asked Mrs Ladd what they meant and was told they were marks carved by Roman soldiers, warning their armies not to advance any further, as the Welsh were too wild to conquer. When I asked Mr Ladd about them he said they were Government survey marks!

It was a day we normally would have stayed home from school, for when we awoke it was not only raining heavily, but a cold wind was whipping up, warning of worse things to come. But Rene had become involved in the 'Pirates of Penzance', a special project, devised by Miss Foy who had now become loved by her pupils and the thought of letting her down was abhorrent to Rene. This no doubt influenced Rene's judgement for, when the rain eased a little, she announced we would make the effort and go to school.

Our main problem was still our clothing. We should have had oilskins for our Mackintoshes were barely shower proof and our clothes soon became wet. Our bare legs allowed the water to run into our shoes and socks, but even so, although wet, by walking quickly we were able to create some warmth.

As usual, on arriving at school, we placed our wet woollen gloves and scarves around the smelly paraffin heaters and hung up our raincoats to dry, which they never did. So yet again, we were still damp from the morning's journey when we dressed and left for our walk home.

We soon realised we were in trouble for apart from having to cope with the steep uphill climb we had to contend with strong gusts of wind that not only tried to push us back downhill but also tried to turn us into blocks of ice. The higher we climbed the worse it became and at New England we flung ourselves into the opposite hedgerow as a squall hit us, driving needles of sleet at any unprotected areas of skin. As it continued we began to feel our extremities starting to freeze. I was about to shout into Rene's ear that we would just have to run for shelter in New England when the wind eased and we dragged ourselves back onto the track. We now faced the open space of the mountain, totally without shelter, and we remembered that we would be crossing above the abandoned slate quarry not far below the track. If the wind blew us over the edge it would be certain death as the drop was over a hundred feet with rocks and water at the bottom. We had been warned not to leave the track at this point. It was getting dark early and we were shivering with cold when we decided to make a run for it, at least we might warm up a little. The run was no more than a trot as we were stiff with cold and changed to a walk as the wind picked up. We were in the middle of the open ground when it hit us. Solid lumps of ice driven by gale force freezing winds sent us diving behind a rock. Heads down we curled up into little balls next to each other hugging the wet ground. Our sense of time slipped by as we slowly froze. In my imagination I was soaking in a hot bath when my sister shook me. The wind had abated and we struggled to our feet.

We were miserable and frozen when we entered the house. Mrs Ladd, standing next to the fire preparing the evening meal, told us to warm ourselves and the pain in our fingers and toes, even our noses and ears, was excruciating as our circulation returned. From then on our chilblains remained with us all winter with our fingers and toes remaining swollen and sore.

The *cawl* that night seemed better than usual, and we nearly burnt our feet trying to warm them on the hot rock we took to bed with us on cold winter nights. The rock, having been heated in the oven, was then wrapped in flannel and placed in an old sock. Our wet clothes were placed around the fire, hopefully, to dry for the morning.

Later, we wondered why nobody had shown any concern for us being out in such foul weather but maybe the squalls did not pass through the farm or maybe the thick stone walls of the farmhouse muted the storm. In any case we had seen Benny carry on ploughing in weather that was not much better and with only a corn sack over his head for protection!

From the military point of view we were usually unaware of the war going on during our stay at Dolrannog. The first uniform we saw was when Benny arrived home one day with his Home Guard uniform, a bit of a disappointment for him as he wished to wear the uniform of a Spitfire pilot. This was always to be a non-event because food producers were man powered but he made the most of being a Home Guard and, as in everything else, Benny had to be the best!

The first thing he did was to blanco all his webbing, not once but three times, then he polished and re-polished his boots till the shine would have brought a smile to the face of any sergeant major. Then we all watched in horror as he placed the heavy flat irons to heat on the fire, refusing Mrs Ladd's offer to help, determined to iron the uniform himself.

We couldn't believe our eyes as he wet a large bar of white soap and rubbed it inside the trousers along the crease and did the same to the inside of the sleeves of his tunic. When the irons were really hot he set about pressing his uniform under a damp cloth, creating more steam than a Chinese laundry and causing Mrs Ladd to cry out in alarm as the ominous smell of scorching pervaded the room. Benny repeated this process several times until he was satisfied the creases were holding their knife-like edge. By this time the uniform could almost stand up on its own, it was so stiff! Any knight of old would have gladly worn it as his suit of armour. Luckily for Benny, it was all downhill to the village since pedalling a bike was well nigh impossible in the now stiffened trousers.

The crowning glory was the cap. This had also been stiffened by Benny who, after greasing back his hair, placed the front point of the forage cap at exactly one inch over his right eyebrow, as per regulations. However, he wore it at such a crazy angle on the right side of his head that it was only able to stay on with the support of his right ear. Benny was determined to be the smartest of his squad even if he was the youngest, and he was already the best shot.

At the other end of the valley was the best known secret of the war, Tre-cŵn. Dug into the side of the valley were miles of tunnels filled with 'munitions. Everyone knew about it, even the Germans. Lord Haw Haw, the

242

German propaganda minister, had even broadcast the fact that they knew it was there and stated that it would be destroyed.

So Newport had to be defended against a possible seaborn raid or invasion. Lengths of rusty railway line were driven into the shallow waters of the bay, the theory being that the bottom of any landing craft would be ripped open on contact with one. A row of land mines was placed along the edge of the beach and fenced in by barbed wire. A concrete bunker was erected in a position overlooking the bay and, day and night, the Home Guard patrolled the area. Benny spent most nights at the bunkhouse which he thoroughly enjoyed. Theoretically, the men were able to sleep most of the night, taking it in turns to patrol, so that they could still work during the day.

At first everyone was alert and apprehensive and the odd sheep or rabbit that strayed through the barbed wire accidentally setting off a land mine caused a major panic but as the war progressed and the tide changed the evening attendance at the bunker resembled more a social club gathering than a military undertaking. Equipment not to be found in any quartermaster's store began to appear, like dart boards and beer mugs.

A German plane was reported flying over the area one night dropping its bombs; it may have been lost or trying to flee to Ireland but in case it was looking for Tre-cŵn a mobile ack-ack unit was camped on the mountain for two weeks. Unfortunately, the weather was foul and no aircraft could fly anyway as the visibility was zero. It was certainly the wrong time and place to be under canvas but the local farmers took it in turns to invite the soldiers into their homes for a hot evening meal.

They were a quiet bunch of about ten men and they looked wet and miserable as they walked into the kitchen at Dolrannog. Mrs Ladd had a big fire roaring, from which, to her disappointment, they kept as far away as they could, saying they didn't want to get too warm before returning to their cold, wet tents. We enjoyed the conversation in English even though some of the soldiers spoke with accents we found hard to understand. They left behind some magazines which was a real treat for us as were the rabbit pies Mrs Ladd had cooked for them, not that there were many left over for us.

After two weeks of doing nothing they packed up and left and I just hoped that they had some good memories to take with them. Winter is not the ideal time to be camping half way up a mountain in Wales!

Ironically, as it turned it was not the German army but our own soldiers who came closest to doing us harm. Rene and I had just left the farmhouse and were on our way to school when it happened. We were in that part of the lane which was bordered on both sides by low walls and high hedgerows, completely screening the fields on either side from our view in the same way as we were out of sight to anyone in the fields.

A ground mist made visibility difficult in low lying places and was quite thick in the lane which was somewhat sunken at this point. The mist had an eerie effect on the landscape, muffling sound with only our footsteps breaking the silence. I remarked on this to Rene and we paused and listened. As if to prove me a liar, we heard a rumbling noise in the distance, which at first we thought was thunder, but as we proceeded the noise grew louder. We became alarmed as the ground started to tremble and a deafening roar surrounded us as we stood in the middle of the lane unable to see what was making the noise. Then, in fright, we watched as two tanks burst through the hedgerow, scattering rocks everywhere; one on each side of us and missing us by only a couple of feet. Without hesitating they crashed through the opposite bank and disappeared in seconds as they headed up the mountain. Uncertain if they were German tanks or ours we were shaking with fear as we ran back to the house, bursting into the kitchen and causing Mrs Ladd to spill her cup of tea.

Mr Ladd had to restrain Benny, who wanted to put on his uniform and do a reconnoitre, reminding him that we had no news of a German invasion. As usual, he was right and we later learned about tank manoeuvres taking place some miles away from where these two had become lost. We had been lucky, but I wondered what would have happened if Mr Ladd had been taking the milk to the truck at that time, it took Mr Ladd and Benny several days to repair the wall, and the scars remained long after we left Dolrannog.

Apart from Mr Davies, the Post, we did see one other uniform at Dolrannog and that was the uniform worn by the Women's Land army. A canvas covered army utility arrived one day and out stepped a very pretty young lady. She looked most attractive in her uniform of riding breeches, green jumper and a wide brimmed hat from under which long blonde hair fell around her shoulders. She announced that it was her job to inspect all the local farms for rat infestation, the theory being if all the rats were eliminated by poisoning, food production would increase.

I didn't think it was a very nice job for a young lady but she seemed to enjoy herself and there was a war on. Benny was most helpful and showed her all around the farm, spending a lot of time in the loft over the cowshed, which I thought strange as I'd never ever seen a rat there! She must have done a good job though, for when another W.L.A. lady arrived to check a few weeks later it only took her about ten minutes to do her inspection and Benny never even had to help her although she was a lot older and quite plump!

Cold squalls again swept across the mountain sending the cattle and sheep scurrying for what little shelter there was. Since it wasn't a school day, we were inside the house waiting for the weather to clear when Mr Ladd walked in shaking the rain from his hat and coat and looking rather worried. We managed to follow the conversation between him and Mrs Ladd well enough to ascertain that Benny and Turpin were missing but half the problem disappeared when Benny walked in. He had only been over to see Emrys but he had walked not ridden the horse. The men went out to double check and found that a gate, which was rather rickety and in need of repair, had given way allowing Turpin to wander off up the mountain. Mrs Ladd added to their fears by saying that if he joined the wild horses he would be gone forever. Benny would have to go and find him.

It was morning tea time when Benny left, rope in hand. The weather had improved somewhat, but by the afternoon there were more squalls and it started to get dark early, so Mr and Mrs Ladd looked relieved to hear the clip clop of a horse being led into the yard. Mr Ladd shouted to Benny from the porch then went back inside but Rene and I took advantage of a break in the clouds which allowed a watery moon to shine on the scene and went outside. Now Rene was still very fond of Turpin even though she had not ridden him since her fall. She would make a fuss of him and feed him whenever she saw him, not that he responded in any way to her affection and Benny would remonstrate with Rene saying Turpin was a working horse and not a bloody pet!

By now Benny was tired, wet, cold and hungry and Turpin apparently had given him a merry dance across the mountain, so when Rene went up to make a fuss of Turpin and ignored Benny, he became very angry and, picking up a branch of a small tree from the woodpile, he laid into Turpin. The horse was more frightened than hurt, rearing up on its hind legs, neighing loudly and trying to pull away from Benny, who was now also under attack from Rene. She was screaming at Benny to stop whilst trying to grab the stick from his hand and at the same time scratch his eyes out. Benny was too strong and continued to lay into the horse, holding Rene at bay with one hand which she promptly bit. Mr and Mrs Ladd came running out on hearing all the commotion. Mr Ladd told Benny to stop hitting Turpin and Mrs Ladd told Rene to stop biting Benny. Rene was now quite hysterical and was led away by Mrs Ladd. Benny pointed out the scratch mark on his face and the bite marks on his hand as Mr Ladd took Turpin from him and quietly led him to the stable. On entering the house, Benny was white with anger and carried out a heated conversation with his mother and Mr Ladd had to raise his voice to restore order when he came in from the cold. I just worried how much more my sister could cope with.

Next day Mrs Ladd told us we were not to interfere with the running of the farm since we obviously didn't understand. She said this horse needed to be punished as it had done wrong to wander off. Rene was normally slow to answer back but this time was quick to point out that it was the horse who didn't understand that he was doing wrong and if the gate had been fixed it would never have happened. But Mrs Ladd had the final word, pointing out that Benny had probably suffered more than the horse and telling us not to go near the horses again. I saw Rene bite her lip and wondered if this was the beginning of the end.

It became obvious to me that Rene was unhappy and was becoming withdrawn and I was worried that she might be heading for another breakdown. I also became aware that we were receiving more letters from our mother than usual but Rene was not sharing the contents with me, only assuring me that there was no need for concern and that our parents were still safe and sound. I somehow knew though that Rene was keeping something from me.

It all came to light when Mr Davies, the Post, delivered the mail which included letters from my mother for Rene and for Mrs Ladd. I watched Mrs Ladd adjust her glasses on the end of her nose before reading her letter and was astonished to see her become most upset as she turned accusingly towards Rene, demanding to know why she had not been told that our mother was on her way to remove us from Dolrannog. Rene could only turn bright red and look at the floor. She had obviously known that it was imminent.

We quickly escaped from Mrs Ladd who was very angry that our mother had given her such short notice. Trying her hardest to compose herself, Rene then opened our letter from Mother. After working out the days and dates Rene told me that our mother had already arrived in the village and was picking us up in the morning. It took a lot of guts for Rene to tell Mrs Ladd this and the evening meal was a grim affair indeed, with Rene trying to answer all the questions as to why our mother was taking us away so suddenly from Dolrannog.

We were shaking with shock and excitement as we went up to bed that night. Was this really to be the last time we would sleep together in the big feather bed? Our prayers were rather mixed up that night but one thing we did ask God to do, was to let our mother and Mrs Ladd part company on friendly terms in the morning.

Sleep was slow to come as we lay with our imaginations running riot. We both just hoped that mother had not made any hasty decisions that we would all later regret. We would soon find out.

On waking in the morning the full realisation that we were leaving Dolrannog very shortly, left us feeling like trespassers. Rene again carefully checked the dates given by our mother in her letter to make sure we had the right day. We decided to make the bed as usual before going out the back for our morning ablutions. On going downstairs we found Mrs Ladd, not at the stove where she usually sat preparing breakfast, but ironing some clean clothes for Rene and me, which she told us to put on after our wash and breakfast.

Neither of us was hungry and we nearly gagged on our

hard boiled egg as Benny and Mr Ladd joined us at the breakfast table. Benny, as usual, had plenty to say and was very critical of our sudden departure before Mr Ladd shut him up. We were very glad to leave the table to go to our room to pack our two small Globite cases with our meagre belongings. It was still early in the morning and we had not been given the exact time that we would be collected; the letter had merely stated some time in the morning.

We looked around our tiny room for the last time before descending the stairs to wait, aware that farm life was going on as usual. We heard the milk churns being loaded and Mr Ladd came in to wish us good luck and goodbye before he left on his journey down the lane but we were still waiting two hours later when he returned. We were still waiting two hours after that when Mrs Ladd started preparing lunch; without a doubt, it was the longest morning of our lives.

Rene was trying to persuade Mrs Ladd not to set places at the table for us, saying we could have lunch with our mother, when we heard the sound of an engine and the taxi drove into the yard. Mr Ladd and Benny were not around and,resisting the impulse to dash outside, Rene and I waited until Mrs Ladd had taken off her apron and patted her hair in place before the three of us emerged from the house together. It was cold and damp outside and the windows of the taxi were steamed up making it hard it see inside. The engine was left running and was rather noisy, making it hard to hear but the driver was leaning out of his window and carrying on a rapid crossfire of questions and answers with Mrs Ladd.

Peering through the obscured glass into the back of the

taxi we were astonished to find it empty, as was the front passenger seat; the driver was the sole occupant. Mrs Ladd now shouted at the driver before turning to us and saying that our mother was waiting for us in the village. There was no doubt about Mrs Ladd's resentment towards our mother when she said that she hadn't the good manners to come and thank her in person for looking after us for all this time, and we couldn't help but inwardly agree with her. It started to pour with rain so our goodbyes were short and none of us could tell whether it was raindrops or tears running down our cheeks. Mrs Ladd's last words, reflecting her true nature and showing love and forgiveness, were to assure us that there would always be a home for us at Dolrannog.

A storm developed as we drove down the mountain. Strong gusts of wind tried to blow us off the track and pouring rain made visibility almost impossible, even with the wipers. Rene and I did not even have to try to see out, we knew exactly where we were. After walking the track for eighteen months we knew every bump, stick and stone and a feeling of relief overcame us as we sat snug in the back of the taxi; relief that we would never have to walk that journey again, in any weather, fair or foul.

As we approached the village the storm passed over and mother was waiting for us outside the entrance to the hotel as we pulled up. We rushed to her. With our few belongings we entered the lounge and sat at the table closest to the fire. A young lady bought us tea and cakes and mother told us we had half an hour to wait for the bus to the station, which would give us time to talk.

A mouthful of cake stopped me from asking the first

question and allowed Rene to speak. I could see the weight of her responsibilities lift from her shoulders as, with confidence, she questioned mother as to why she had not informed Mrs Ladd of her plans sooner, and why she had not arrived in the taxi to thank Mrs Ladd for looking after us. In reply mother tried to gloss things over in her usual manner, blaming the bombing for delaying the mail and calling the taxi driver stupid for not understanding her instructions, but he had not seemed stupid to me.

Mother told us we could now safely live in our house again as there was no longer a risk of invasion. In fact, she said the next invasion would be by the Allies when they landed in Europe and also that England now had supremacy of the skies following the Battle of Britain.

It was lucky that I had swallowed my cake before I asked about school, otherwise I would have choked to death on it when mother told me I was being sent to a boarding school. My heart sank and I nearly burst into tears. After waiting all this time to go home I was to be sent away again and on my own this time.

Mother said I was privileged to be able to attend such an expensive school and that I would be able to travel home in the school holidays. My father, having realised that my education was barely basic and that the war would come to an end someday, had deemed it necessary for me to receive a good education as well as discipline. I had read about boarding schools like the one that Tom Brown attended with the bullying, cold showers and the cane and I knew I was in deep trouble. After living high on a Welsh mountain and acquiring a Welsh accent and customs, I knew that I would be the odd one out.

As we travelled the same switchback road to Fishguard, my mind took me back to the first time I had made the journey on that first night in Wales, and I actually started to tremble as I stood once again on the platform at the station. A Thomas the Tank engine was waiting quietly with its one antiquated carriage. This quickly filled up and I was once again surrounded by the Welsh language. It must have been market day somewhere because all the people seemed to be carrying bags of produce and there was quite a variety of poultry sticking their heads out of home made cages.

As we progressed to Swansea with people getting on and off along the way, I recognised some of the scenery that we had passed, now almost two years before that. There was a delay in Swansea and we waited for the proper train which would take us on the rest of our journey. As it pulled into the station I wondered if it was the same engine which had brought us to Wales; it looked the same but I could not remember the name.

We were now seated in a compartment with other adults and I listened to their conversation about the war as they discussed the headlines of a newspaper. Hitler wasn't done for yet and England was still being bombed. I began to wish I could have stayed in Wales and a feeling of darkness came over me. Then I realised we were in a long tunnel and I remembered that this was the tunnel under the river Severn, and that when we came out at the other end we would be in England.

APPENDIX 2001

CAPT FOSKETT did not return to England after the war, preferring to stay in Germany with his lady.

MRS FOSKETT stayed on in the home at Battle.

Rene became a schoolteacher then mother to four children. Her health was never strong.

Ken left England at nineteen to live in Australia. First trip home, after 26 years, in 1976.

Benny and his wife Gwenny retired to the village. Their youngest son still runs Dolrannog.